MW00609670

www.EffortlessMath.com

... So Much More Online!

✓ FREE Math lessons

✓ More Math learning books!

✓ Mathematics Worksheets

✓ Online Math Tutors

Need a PDF version of this book?

Please visit www.EffortlessMath.com

STAAR Grade 7 Math Preparation 2020 - 2021

STAAR Grade 7 Math Workbook + 2 Full-Length STAAR Grade 7 Math Practice Tests

By

Reza Nazari & Ava Ross

Copyright © 2020

Reza Nazari & Ava Ross

All rights reserved. No part of this publication may be reproduced, stored in a retrieval system, or transmitted in any form or by any means, electronic, mechanical, photocopying, recording, scanning, or otherwise, except as permitted under Section 107 or 108 of the 1976 United States Copyright Ac, without permission of the author.

All inquiries should be addressed to:

info@effortlessMath.com

www.EffortlessMath.com

ISBN: 978-1-64612-402-2

Published by: Effortless Math Education

www.EffortlessMath.com

Description

STAAR Grade 7 Math Preparation 2020 - 2021, which reflects the 2020 - 2021 test guidelines, is prepared by top STAAR Math instructors and test prep experts to help test takers succeed on the STAAR Math Test. This STAAR Math prep new edition has been updated to replicate questions appearing on the most recent STAAR math tests. Upon completion of this comprehensive STAAR Math prep book, you will have a solid foundation and sufficient practice to ace the STAAR Math test. **This prep book is your ticket to scoring higher on STAAR Grade 7 Math.**

Not only does this perfect and comprehensive STAAR Math book include everything you will ever need to conquer the STAAR Math test, but it also contains two full-length and realistic STAAR Math practice tests that reflect the format and question types on the STAAR to help you check your exam-readiness and identify where you need more practice.

STAAR Grade 7 Math Preparation 2020 - 2021 contains many exciting and unique features to help you improve your test scores, including:

- ✓ Content 100% aligned with the 2020 STAAR test
- ✓ Complete coverage of all STAAR Math concepts and topics which you will be tested
- ✓ Numerous STAAR math practice questions in both multiple-choice and grid-in formats with answers grouped by topic, so you can focus on your weak areas
- ✓ Abundant Math skill-building exercises to help test-takers approach different question types that might be unfamiliar to them
- ✓ 2 full-length practice tests (featuring new question types) with detailed answers

This STAAR Math prep book and other Effortless Math Education books are used by thousands of students each year to help them review core content areas, brush-up in math, discover their strengths and weaknesses, and achieve their best scores on the STAAR test.

About the Author

Reza Nazari is the author of more than 100 Math learning books including:
– **Math and Critical Thinking Challenges:** For the Middle and High School Student
– **GED Math in 30 Days**
– **ASVAB Math Workbook 2018 - 2019**
– **Effortless Math Education Workbooks**
– **and many more Mathematics books …**

Reza is also an experienced Math instructor and a test–prep expert who has been tutoring students since 2008. Reza is the founder of Effortless Math Education, a tutoring company that has helped many students raise their standardized test scores—and attend the colleges of their dreams. Reza provides an individualized custom learning plan and the personalized attention that makes a difference in how students view math.

You can contact Reza via email at:
reza@EffortlessMath.com

Find Reza's professional profile at:
goo.gl/zoC9rJ

Contents

Chapter 1:

Fractions and Decimals

Topics that you'll practice in this chapter:

- ✓ Simplifying Fractions
- ✓ Adding and Subtracting Fractions
- ✓ Multiplying and Dividing Fractions
- ✓ Adding and Subtract Mixed Numbers
- ✓ Multiplying and Dividing Mixed Numbers
- ✓ Adding and Subtracting Decimals
- ✓ Multiplying and Dividing Decimals
- ✓ Comparing Decimals
- ✓ Rounding Decimals

Name: ....

Date: ....

Topic	*Simplifying Fractions*
Notes	✓ Evenly divide both the top and bottom of the fraction by $2, 3, 5, 7, \ldots$ etc. ✓ Continue until you can't go any further.
Example	*Simplify* $\frac{36}{48}$ **Solution:** To simplify $\frac{36}{48}$, find a number that both 36 and 48 are divisible by. Both are divisible by 12. Then: $\frac{36}{48} = \frac{36 \div 12}{48 \div 12} = \frac{3}{4}$

Your Turn!	1) $\frac{2}{18} =$	2) $\frac{22}{66} =$
	3) $\frac{12}{48} =$	4) $\frac{11}{99} =$
	5) $\frac{15}{75} =$	6) $\frac{25}{100} =$
	7) $\frac{16}{72} =$	8) $\frac{32}{96} =$
	9) $\frac{14}{77} =$	10) $\frac{60}{84} =$

| Name: .... | Date: .... |

Topic	*Adding and Subtracting Fractions*
Notes	✓ For "like" fractions (fractions with the same denominator), add or subtract the numerators and write the answer over the common denominator. ✓ Find equivalent fractions with the same denominator before you can add or subtract fractions with different denominators. ✓ Adding and Subtracting with the same denominator: $$\frac{a}{b} + \frac{c}{b} = \frac{a+c}{b} , \frac{a}{b} - \frac{c}{b} = \frac{a-c}{b}$$ ✓ Adding and Subtracting fractions with different denominators: $$\frac{a}{b} + \frac{c}{d} = \frac{ad+bc}{bd} , \frac{a}{b} - \frac{c}{d} = \frac{ad-bc}{bd}$$
Example	1) *Find the sum.* $\frac{3}{5} + \frac{2}{3}$ **Solution:** $\frac{3}{5} + \frac{2}{3} = \frac{(3)3+(5)(2)}{5\times3} = \frac{19}{15}$ 2) *Subtract.* $\frac{4}{7} - \frac{3}{7}$ **Solution:** $\frac{4}{7} - \frac{3}{7} = \frac{1}{7}$

Your Turn!	1) $\frac{3}{5} + \frac{2}{7} =$	2) $\frac{7}{9} - \frac{4}{7} =$
	3) $\frac{4}{9} + \frac{5}{8} =$	4) $\frac{5}{8} - \frac{2}{5} =$
	5) $\frac{2}{5} + \frac{1}{6} =$	6) $\frac{2}{3} - \frac{1}{4} =$
	7) $\frac{8}{9} + \frac{5}{7} =$	8) $\frac{6}{7} - \frac{5}{9} =$

Name: ....

Date: ....

Topic	*Multiplying and Dividing Fractions*
Notes	✓ Multiplying fractions: multiply the top numbers and multiply the bottom numbers. ✓ Dividing fractions: Keep, Change, Flip Keep first fraction, change division sign to multiplication, and flip the numerator and denominator of the second fraction. Then, solve!
Examples	1) *Multiply.* $\frac{2}{5} \times \frac{3}{4} =$ **Solution:** Multiply the top numbers and multiply the bottom numbers. $\frac{2}{5} \times \frac{3}{4} = \frac{2 \times 3}{5 \times 4} = \frac{6}{20}$, simplify: $\frac{6}{20} = \frac{6 \div 2}{20 \div 2} = \frac{3}{10}$ 2) *Divide.* $\frac{2}{5} \div \frac{3}{4} =$ **Solution:** Keep first fraction, change division sign to multiplication, and flip the numerator and denominator of the second fraction. Then: $\frac{2}{5} \div \frac{3}{4} = \frac{2}{5} \times \frac{4}{3} = \frac{2 \times 4}{5 \times 3} = \frac{8}{15}$
Your Turn!	1) $\frac{5}{9} \times \frac{4}{7} =$ 2) $\frac{3}{5} \div \frac{2}{3} =$ 3) $\frac{2}{7} \times \frac{3}{5} =$ 4) $\frac{2}{5} \div \frac{7}{12} =$ 5) $\frac{1}{7} \times \frac{4}{9} =$ 6) $\frac{2}{9} \div \frac{3}{7} =$ 7) $\frac{2}{5} \times \frac{6}{7} =$ 8) $\frac{1}{4} \div \frac{2}{5} =$

Name: ....   Date: ....

Topic	*Adding Mixed Numbers*
Notes	Use the following steps for adding mixed numbers. ✓ Add whole numbers of the mixed numbers. ✓ Add the fractions of each mixed number. ✓ Find the Least Common Denominator (LCD) if necessary. ✓ Add whole numbers and fractions. ✓ Write your answer in lowest terms.
Example	*Add mixed numbers.* $1\frac{1}{2} + 2\frac{2}{3} =$ **Solution:** Rewriting our equation with parts separated, $1 + \frac{1}{2} + 2 + \frac{2}{3}$ Add whole numbers: $1 + 2 = 3$ Add fractions: $\frac{1}{2} + \frac{2}{3} = \frac{3}{6} + \frac{4}{6} = \frac{7}{6} = 1\frac{1}{6}$, Now, combine the whole and fraction parts: $3 + 1 + \frac{1}{6} = 4\frac{1}{6}$
Your Turn!	1) $1\frac{1}{12} + 2\frac{3}{4} =$ 2) $3\frac{5}{8} + 1\frac{1}{4} =$ 3) $1\frac{1}{10} + 2\frac{2}{5} =$ 4) $2\frac{5}{6} + 2\frac{2}{9} =$ 5) $2\frac{2}{7} + 1\frac{2}{21} =$ 6) $1\frac{3}{8} + 3\frac{2}{3} =$ 7) $3\frac{1}{5} + 1\frac{2}{8} =$ 8) $3\frac{1}{2} + 2\frac{3}{7} =$

Name: ....

Date: ....

Topic	***Subtracting Mixed Numbers***
Notes	Use the following steps for subtracting mixed numbers. ✓ Convert mixed numbers into improper fractions. $a\frac{c}{b} = \frac{ab+c}{b}$ ✓ Find equivalent fractions with the same denominator for unlike fractions (fractions with different denominators) ✓ Subtract the second fraction from the first one. ✓ Write your answer in lowest terms and convert it into a mixed number if the answer is an improper fraction.
Example	*Subtract.* $5\frac{1}{2} - 2\frac{2}{3} =$ **Solution:** Convert mixed numbers into fractions: $5\frac{1}{2} = \frac{5\times2+1}{5} = \frac{11}{2}$ and $2\frac{2}{3} = \frac{2\times3+2}{4} = \frac{8}{3}$, these two fractions are "unlike" fractions. (they have different denominators). Find equivalent fractions with the same denominator. Use this formula: $\frac{a}{b} - \frac{c}{d} = \frac{ad-bc}{bd}$ $\frac{11}{2} - \frac{8}{3} = \frac{(11)(3)-(2)(8)}{2\times3} = \frac{33-16}{6} = \frac{17}{6}$, the answer is an improper fraction, convert it into a mixed number. $\frac{17}{6} = 2\frac{5}{6}$
Your Turn!	1) $2\frac{2}{5} - 1\frac{1}{3} =$ 2) $3\frac{5}{8} - 2\frac{1}{3} =$ 3) $6\frac{1}{4} - 1\frac{2}{7} =$ 4) $8\frac{2}{3} - 1\frac{1}{4} =$ 5) $8\frac{3}{4} - 1\frac{3}{8} =$ 6) $2\frac{3}{8} - 1\frac{2}{3} =$ 7) $13\frac{2}{7} - 1\frac{2}{21} =$ 8) $5\frac{1}{2} - 2\frac{3}{7} =$

Name: ....

Date: ....

Topic	*Multiplying Mixed Numbers*
Notes	✓ Convert the mixed numbers into fractions. $a\frac{c}{b} = a + \frac{c}{b} = \frac{ab+c}{b}$ ✓ Multiply fractions and simplify if necessary. $\frac{a}{b} \times \frac{c}{d} = \frac{a \times c}{b \times d}$ ✓ If the answer is an improper fraction (numerator is bigger than denominator), convert it into a mixed number.
Example	*Multiply* $2\frac{1}{4} \times 3\frac{1}{2}$ **Solution:** Convert mixed numbers into fractions: $2\frac{1}{4} = \frac{2\times4+1}{4} = \frac{9}{4}$ and $3\frac{1}{2} = \frac{3\times2+1}{2} = \frac{7}{2}$ Multiply two fractions: $\frac{9}{4} \times \frac{7}{2} = \frac{9\times7}{4\times2} = \frac{63}{8}$ The answer is an improper fraction. Convert it into a mixed number: $$\frac{63}{8} = 7\frac{7}{8}$$
Your Turn!	1) $5\frac{2}{3} \times 2\frac{2}{9} =$ 2) $4\frac{1}{6} \times 5\frac{3}{7} =$ 3) $3\frac{1}{3} \times 3\frac{3}{4} =$ 4) $2\frac{2}{9} \times 6\frac{1}{3} =$ 5) $2\frac{2}{7} \times 4\frac{3}{5} =$ 6) $1\frac{4}{7} \times 9\frac{1}{2} =$ 7) $4\frac{1}{8} \times 3\frac{2}{3} =$ 8) $6\frac{2}{3} \times 1\frac{1}{4} =$

Name: ....   Date: ....

Topic	*Dividing Mixed Numbers*
Notes	✓ Convert the mixed numbers into improper fractions. $$a\frac{c}{b} = a + \frac{c}{b} = \frac{ab + c}{b}$$ ✓ Divide fractions and simplify if necessary.
Example	*Solve.* $2\frac{1}{3} \div 1\frac{1}{4} =$ **Solution:** Converting mixed numbers to fractions: $2\frac{1}{3} \div 1\frac{1}{4} = \frac{7}{3} \div \frac{5}{4}$ Keep, Change, Flip: $\frac{7}{3} \div \frac{5}{4} = \frac{7}{3} \times \frac{4}{5} = \frac{7\times4}{3\times5} = \frac{28}{15} = 1\frac{13}{15}$

Your Turn!	1) $3\frac{2}{7} \div 2\frac{1}{4} =$	2) $4\frac{2}{9} \div 1\frac{5}{6} =$
	3) $4\frac{2}{3} \div 3\frac{2}{5} =$	4) $5\frac{4}{5} \div 4\frac{3}{4} =$
	5) $1\frac{8}{9} \div 2\frac{3}{7} =$	6) $3\frac{3}{8} \div 2\frac{2}{5} =$
	7) $4\frac{1}{5} \div 3\frac{1}{9} =$	8) $4\frac{2}{3} \div 1\frac{8}{9} =$
	9) $5\frac{2}{3} \div 3\frac{3}{7} =$	10) $7\frac{1}{2} \div 5\frac{1}{3} =$

Name:	Date: ....

Topic	*Adding and Subtracting Decimals*
Notes	✓ Line up the numbers. ✓ Add zeros to have same number of digits for both numbers if necessary. ✓ Add or subtract using column addition or subtraction.
Examples	1) *Add.* $2.6 + 5.33 =$ **Solution:** First line up the numbers: $\begin{array}{r} 2.6 \\ +\,5.33 \\ \hline \end{array}$ →Add zeros to have same number of digits for both numbers. $\begin{array}{r} 2.60 \\ +\,5.33 \\ \hline \;\;\; \end{array}$ → Start with the hundredths place. $0 + 3 =$ 2, $\begin{array}{r} 2.60 \\ +\,5.33 \\ \hline 3 \end{array}$ → Continue with tenths place. $6 + 3 = 9$, $\begin{array}{r} 2.60 \\ +\,5.33 \\ \hline .93 \end{array}$ → Add the ones place. $2 + 5 = 7$, $\begin{array}{r} 2.60 \\ +\,5.33 \\ \hline 7.93 \end{array}$ 2) *Subtract.* $4.79 - 3.13 =$ $\begin{array}{r} 4.79 \\ -\,3.13 \\ \hline \end{array}$ **Solution:** Start with the hundredths place. $9 - 3 = 6$, $\begin{array}{r} 4.79 \\ -\,3.13 \\ \hline 6 \end{array}$, continue with tenths place. $7 - 1 = 6$, $\begin{array}{r} 4.79 \\ -\,3.13 \\ \hline .66 \end{array}$, subtract the ones place. $4 - 3 = 1$, $\begin{array}{r} 4.79 \\ -\,3.13 \\ \hline 1.66 \end{array}$
Your Turn!	1) $48.13 + 20.15 =$ ⫼ 2) $78.14 - 65.19 =$
	3) $38.19 + 24.18 =$ ⫼ 4) $57.26 - 43.54 =$
	5) $27.89 + 46.13 =$ ⫼ 6) $49.65 - 32.78 =$

Name: ....   Date: ....

Topic	*Multiplying and Dividing Decimals*
Notes	For Multiplication: ✓ Ignore the decimal point and set up and multiply the numbers as you do with whole numbers. ✓ Count the total number of decimal places in both factors. ✓ Place the decimal point in the product. For Division: ✓ If the divisor is not a whole number, move decimal point to right to make it a whole number. Do the same for dividend. ✓ Divide similar to whole numbers.
Examples	1) Find the product. $1.2 \times 2.3 =$ **Solution:** Set up and multiply the numbers as you do with whole numbers. Line up the numbers: $\frac{12}{\times 23} \rightarrow$ Multiply: $\frac{\substack{12 \\ \times 23}}{276} \rightarrow$ Count the total number of decimal places in both of the factors. There are two decimal digits. Then: $1.2 \times 2.3 = 2.76$ 2) Find the quotient. $5.6 \div 0.8 =$ **Solution:** The divisor is not a whole number. Multiply it by 10 to get 8. $\rightarrow 0.8 \times 10 = 8$ Do the same for the dividend to get 56 $\rightarrow 5.6 \times 10 = 56$ Now, divide: $56 \div 8 = 7$. The answer is 7.
Your Turn!	1) $1.13 \times 0.7 =$ 2) $48.8 \div 8 =$ 3) $0.9 \times 0.68 =$ 4) $66.8 \div 0.2 =$ 5) $0.18 \times 0.5 =$ 6) $37.2 \div 100 =$

Name: ....

Date: ....

Topic	*Comparing Decimals*
Notes	Decimals: is a fraction written in a special form. For example, instead of writing $\frac{1}{2}$ you can write **0.5**. For comparing decimals: ✓ Compare each digit of two decimals in the same place value. ✓ Start from left. Compare hundreds, tens, ones, tenth, hundredth, etc. ✓ To compare numbers, use these symbols: - Equal to $=$, Less than $<$, Greater than $>$ Greater than or equal $\geq$, Less than or equal $\leq$
Examples	1) **Compare** 0.40 and 0.04. **Solution:** 0.40 *is greater than* 0.04, because the tenth place of 0.40 is 4, but the tenth place of 0.04 is zero. Then: $0.40 > 0.04$ 2) **Compare** 0.0912 and 0.912. **Solution:** 0.912 *is greater than* 0.0912, because the tenth place of 0.912 is 9, but the tenth place of 0.0912 is zero. Then: $0.0912 < 0.912$

Your Turn!	1) 0.91 ☐ 0.95	2) 1.79 ☐ 1.80
	3) 19.1 ☐ 19.09	4) 2.45 ☐ 2.089
	5) 1.258 ☐ 12.58	6) 0.89 ☐ 0.890
	7) 3.871 ☐ 2.998	8) 0.567 ☐ 0.756

Name:	Date: ....

Topic	*Rounding Decimals*
Notes	✓ We can round decimals to a certain accuracy or number of decimal places. ✓ Let's review place values: For example: **35.4817** 3: tens 5: ones 4: tenths 8: hundredths 1: thousandths 7:tens thousandths ✓ To round a decimal, find the place value you'll round to. ✓ Find the digit to the right of the place value you're rounding to. If it is 5 or bigger, add 1 to the place value you're rounding to and remove all digits on its right side. If the digit to the right of the place value is less than 5, keep the place value and remove all digits on the right.
Example	Round **12.8365** to the hundredth place value. First look at the next place value to the right, (thousandths). It's 6 and it is greater than 5. Thus add 1 to the digit in the hundredth place. It is 3. $\rightarrow 3 + 1 = 4$, then, the answer is 12.84

Round each number to the *underlined* place value.

1) $32.5\underline{4}8 =$	2) $2.3\underline{2}6 =$
3) $55.\underline{4}23 =$	4) $25.\underline{6}2 =$
5) $11.\underline{2}65 =$	6) $33.5\underline{0}5 =$
7) $3.5\underline{8}9 =$	8) $8.0\underline{1}9 =$

Your Turn!

Answers – Chapter 1

Simplifying Fractions

1) $\frac{1}{9}$

2) $\frac{1}{3}$

3) $\frac{1}{4}$

4) $\frac{1}{9}$

5) $\frac{1}{5}$

6) $\frac{1}{4}$

7) $\frac{2}{9}$

8) $\frac{1}{3}$

9) $\frac{2}{11}$

10) $\frac{5}{7}$

Adding and Subtracting Fractions

1) $\frac{31}{35}$

2) $\frac{13}{63}$

3) $\frac{77}{72}$

4) $\frac{9}{40}$

5) $\frac{17}{30}$

6) $\frac{5}{12}$

7) $\frac{101}{63}$

8) $\frac{19}{63}$

Multiplying and Dividing Fractions

1) $\frac{20}{63}$

2) $\frac{9}{10}$

3) $\frac{6}{35}$

4) $\frac{24}{35}$

5) $\frac{4}{63}$

6) $\frac{14}{27}$

7) $\frac{12}{35}$

8) $\frac{5}{8}$

Adding Mixed Numbers

1) $3\frac{5}{6}$

2) $4\frac{7}{8}$

3) $3\frac{1}{2}$

4) $5\frac{1}{18}$

5) $3\frac{8}{21}$

6) $5\frac{1}{24}$

7) $4\frac{9}{20}$

8) $5\frac{13}{14}$

Subtracting Mixed Numbers

1) $1\frac{1}{15}$
2) $1\frac{7}{24}$
3) $4\frac{27}{28}$
4) $7\frac{5}{12}$

5) $7\frac{3}{8}$
6) $\frac{17}{24}$
7) $12\frac{4}{21}$
8) $3\frac{1}{4}$

Multiplying Mixed Numbers

1) $12\frac{16}{27}$
2) $22\frac{13}{21}$
3) $12\frac{1}{2}$
4) $14\frac{2}{27}$

5) $10\frac{18}{35}$
6) $14\frac{13}{14}$
7) $15\frac{1}{8}$
8) $8\frac{1}{3}$

Dividing Mixed numbers

1) $1\frac{29}{63}$
2) $2\frac{10}{33}$
3) $1\frac{19}{51}$
4) $1\frac{21}{95}$
5) $\frac{7}{9}$

6) $1\frac{13}{32}$
7) $1\frac{7}{20}$
8) $2\frac{8}{17}$
9) $1\frac{47}{72}$
10) $1\frac{13}{32}$

Adding and Subtracting Decimals

1) 68.28
2) 12.95
3) 62.37

4) 13.72
5) 74.02
6) 16.87

Multiplying and Dividing Decimals

1) 0.791
2) 6.1
3) 0.612

4) 334
5) 0.09
6) 0.372

Comparing Decimals

1) <
2) <
3) >
4) >

5) <
6) =
7) >
8) <

Rounding Decimals

1) 32.25
2) 2.33
3) 55.4
4) 26

5) 11.3
6) 33.51
7) 3.59
8) 8.02

Chapter 2:

Real Numbers and Integers

Topics that you'll practice in this chapter:

✓ Adding and Subtracting Integers

✓ Multiplying and Dividing Integers

✓ Order of Operations

✓ Integers and Absolute Value

Name:		Date: ....

Topic	*Adding and Subtracting Integers*	
Notes	✓ Integers include: zero, counting numbers, and the negative of the counting numbers. $\{... , -3, -2, -1, 0, 1, 2, 3, ...\}$ ✓ Add a positive integer by moving to the right on the number line. ✓ Add a negative integer by moving to the left on the number line. Subtract an integer by adding its opposite.	
Examples	1) Solve. $(4) - (-8) =$ **Solution:** Keep the first number and convert the sign of the second number to its opposite. (change subtraction into addition. Then: $(4) + 8 = 12$ 2) Solve. $42 + (12 - 26) =$ **Solution:** First subtract the numbers in brackets, $12 - 26 = -14$ Then: $42 + (-14) = \rightarrow$ change addition into subtraction: $42 - 14 = 28$	
Your Turn!	1) $-(15) + 12 =$	2) $(-2) + (-10) + 18 =$
	3) $(-13) + 7 =$	4) $3 - (-7) + 14 =$
	5) $(-7) + (-8) =$	6) $16 - (-4 + 8) =$
	7) $4 + (-15) + 2 =$	8) $-(22) - (-4) + 8 =$

Name: ....

Date: ....

Topic	*Multiplying and Dividing Integers*
Notes	Use following rules for multiplying and dividing integers: ✓ (negative) × (negative) = positive ✓ (negative) ÷ (negative) = positive ✓ (negative) × (positive) = negative ✓ (negative) ÷ (positive) = negative ✓ (positive) × (positive) = positive ✓ (positive) ÷ (negative) = negative
Examples	1) Solve. $2 \times (14 - 17) =$ **Solution:** First subtract the numbers in brackets, $14 - 17 = -3 \rightarrow$ $(2) \times (-3) =$ Now use this rule: (positive) × (negative) = negative $(2) \times (-3) = -6$ 2) Solve. $(-7) + (-36 \div 4) =$ **Solution:** First divide -36 by 4, the numbers in brackets, using this rule: (negative) ÷ (positive) = negative Then: $-36 \div 4 = -9$. Now, add -7 and -9: $(-7) + (-9) = -7 - 9 = -16$
Your Turn!	1) $(-7) \times 6 =$ 2) $(-63) \div (-7) =$ 3) $(-11) \times (-3) =$ 4) $81 \div (-9) =$ 5) $(15 - 12) \times (-7) =$ 6) $(-12) \div (3) =$ 7) $4 \times (-9) =$ 8) $(8) \div (-2) =$

Name: ....   **Date:** ....

Topic	*Order of Operation*
Notes	When there is more than one math operation, use PEMDAS: (to memorize this rule, remember the phrase "Please Excuse My Dear Aunt Sally") ✓ Parentheses ✓ Exponents ✓ Multiplication and Division (from left to right) ✓ Addition and Subtraction (from left to right)
Examples	1) Calculate. $(18 - 26) \div (2^4 \div 4) =$ **Solution:** First simplify inside parentheses: $(-8) \div (16 \div 4) = (-8) \div (4)$ Then: $(-8) \div (4) = -2$ 2) Solve. $(-5 \times 7) - (18 - 3^2) =$ **Solution:** First calculate within parentheses: $(-5 \times 7) - (18 - 3^2) = (-35) - (18 - 9)$ Then: $(-35) - (18 - 9) = -35 - 9 = -44$
Your Turn!	1) $(11 \times 4) \div (5 + 6) =$ 2) $(30 \div 5) + (17 - 8) =$ 3) $(-9) + (5 \times 6) + 14 =$ 4) $(-10 \times 5) \div (2^2 + 1) =$ 5) $[-16(32 \div 2^3)] \div 8 =$ 6) $(-7) + (72 \div 3^2) + 12 =$ 7) $[16(32 \div 2^3)] - 4^2 =$ 8) $4^3 + (-5 \times 2^5) + 5 =$

Name:	Date: ....

Topic	*Integers and Absolute Value*
Notes	✓ The absolute value of a number is its distance from zero, in either direction, on the number line. For example, the distance of 9 and -9 from zero on number line is 9. ✓ Absolute value is symbolized by vertical bars, as in $|x|$.
Example	Calculate. $|8-5| \times |12-16| =$ **Solution:** First calculate $|8-5|$, $\to |8-5| = |3|$, the absolute value of 3 is 3, $|3| = 3$ $8 \times |12-16| =$ Now calculate $|12-16|$, $\to |12-16| = |-4|$, the absolute value of -4 is 4, $|-4| = 4$. Then: $3 \times 4 = 12$

Your Turn!	1) $11 - |4-13| =$	2) $14 - |12-19| - |9| =$
	3) $|21| - \frac{|-25|}{5} =$	4) $|30| + \frac{|-49|}{7} =$
	5) $\frac{|7 \times -8|}{4} \times \frac{|-12|}{2} =$	6) $\frac{|10 \times -6|}{5} \times |-9| =$
	7) $\frac{|-20|}{5} \times \frac{|-36|}{6} =$	8) $|-30+6| \times \frac{|-9 \times 4|}{12} =$

Answers – Chapter 2

Adding and Subtracting Integers

1) -3
2) 6
3) -6

4) 24
5) -15
6) 12

7) -9
8) -10

Multiplying and Dividing Integers

1) -42
2) 9
3) 33

4) -9
5) -21
6) -4

7) -36
8) -4

Order of Operations

1) 4
2) 15
3) 35

4) -10
5) -8
6) 13

7) 48
8) -91

Integers and Absolute Value

1) 2
2) -2
3) 16

4) 37
5) 84
6) 108

7) 24
8) 72

Chapter 3:

Proportions, Ratios, and Percent

Topics that you'll practice in this chapter:

✓ Simplifying Ratios

✓ Proportional Ratios

✓ Similarity and Ratios

✓ Percent Problems

✓ Discount, Tax and Tip

✓ Percent of Change

✓ Simple Interest

Name: ....

Date: ....

Topic	*Simplifying Ratios*
Notes	✓ Ratios are used to make comparisons between two numbers. ✓ Ratios can be written as a fraction, using the word "to", or with a colon. ✓ You can calculate equivalent ratios by multiplying or dividing both sides of the ratio by the same number.
Examples	1) Simplify. $18:63 =$ **Solution:** Both numbers 18 and 63 are divisible by $9 \Rightarrow 18 \div 9 = 2$, $63 \div 9 = 7$, Then: $18:63 = 2:7$ 2) Simplify. $\frac{25}{45} =$ **Solution:** Both numbers 25 and 45 are divisible by 5, $\Rightarrow 25 \div 5 = 5$, $45 \div 5 = 9$, Then: $\frac{25}{45} = \frac{5}{9}$
Your Turn!	1) $\frac{4}{32} = -$ 2) $\frac{25}{80} = -$ 3) $\frac{15}{35} = -$ 4) $\frac{42}{54} = -$ 5) $\frac{12}{36} = -$ 6) $\frac{30}{80} = -$ 7) $\frac{18}{24} = -$ 8) $\frac{60}{108} = -$

Name: ....

Date: ....

Topic	*Proportional Ratios*
Notes	✓ Two ratios are proportional if they represent the same relationship. ✓ A proportion means that two ratios are equal. It can be written in two ways: $\quad \frac{a}{b} = \frac{c}{d} \qquad a : b = c : d$
Example	Solve this proportion for x. $\frac{5}{8} = \frac{35}{x}$ **Solution:** Use cross multiplication: $\qquad \frac{5}{8} = \frac{35}{x} \Rightarrow 5 \times x = 8 \times 35 \Rightarrow$ $5x = 280$ Divide to find x: $\quad x = \frac{280}{5} \Rightarrow x = 56$
Your Turn!	1) $\frac{1}{9} = \frac{8}{x} \Rightarrow x = $ ____ 2) $\frac{5}{8} = \frac{25}{x} \Rightarrow x = $ ____ 3) $\frac{3}{11} = \frac{6}{x} \Rightarrow x = $ ____ 4) $\frac{12}{20} = \frac{x}{200} \Rightarrow x = $ ____ 5) $\frac{9}{12} = \frac{27}{x} \Rightarrow x = $ ____ 6) $\frac{14}{16} = \frac{x}{80} \Rightarrow x = $ ____ 7) $\frac{7}{15} = \frac{49}{x} \Rightarrow x = $ ____ 8) $\frac{8}{19} = \frac{32}{x} \Rightarrow x = $ ____

Name:	Date: ....

Topic	**Similarity and Ratios**	
Notes	✓ Two figures are similar if they have the same shape. ✓ Two or more figures are similar if the corresponding angles are equal, and the corresponding sides are in proportion.	
Example	Following triangles are similar. What is the value of unknown side? **Solution:** Find the corresponding sides and write a proportion: $\frac{4}{12} = \frac{x}{9}$. Now, use cross product to solve for x: $\frac{4}{12} = \frac{x}{9} \to 4 \times 9 = 12 \times x \to 36 = 12x$. Divide both sides by 12. Then: $5x = 40 \to \frac{36}{12} = \frac{12x}{12} \to x = 3$. The missing side is 3.	

Your Turn!	1)	2)
	3)	4)
	5)	6)

Name:	Date: ....

Topic	*Percent Problems*

Notes	✓ In each percent problem, we are looking for the base, or part or the percent.
	✓ Use the following equations to find each missing section.
	   ○ Base = Part ÷ Percent
	   ○ Part = Percent × Base
	   ○ Percent = Part ÷ Base

Examples	1) 18 is what percent of 30?
	   Solution: In this problem, we are looking for the percent. Use the following equation:
	   $Percent = Part \div Base \rightarrow Percent = 18 \div 30 = 0.6 = 60\%$
	2) 40 is 20% of what number?
	   Solution: Use the following formula: $Base = Part \div Percent \rightarrow Base = 40 \div 0.20 = 200$
	   40 is 20% of 200.

Your Turn!		
	1) What is 25 percent of 800	2) 26 is what percent of 200? _____
	3) 60 is 5 percent of what number? _____	4) 48 is what percent of 300? _____
	5) 84 is 28 percent of what number? _____	6) 63 is what percent of 700? _____
	7) 96 is 24 percent of what number? _____	8) 40 is what percent of 800? _____

Name: .... **Date:** ....

Topic	*Percent of Increase and Decrease*

Notes	✓ Percent of change (increase or decrease) is a mathematical concept that represents the degree of change over time.
	✓ To find the percentage of increase or decrease:
	  1- New Number – Original Number
	  2- The result ÷ Original Number × 100
	
	Or use this formula: Percent of change = $\frac{new\ number - original\ number}{original\ number} \times 100$

Example	The price of a printer increases from \$40 to \$50. What is the percent increase? **Solution:** Percent of change = $\frac{new\ number - original\ number}{original\ number} \times 100 =$ $\frac{50-40}{40} \times 100 = 25$ The percentage increase is 25. It means that the price of the printer increased 25%.
Your Turn!	1) In a class, the number of students has been increased from 32 to 36. What is the percentage increase? _____ % 2) The price of gasoline rose from \$4.50 to \$5.40 in one month. By what percent did the gas price rise? _____ % 3) A shirt was originally priced at \$65.00. It went on sale for \$52.00. What was the percent that the shirt was discounted? _____ % 4) Jason got a raise, and his hourly wage increased from \$40 to \$52. What is the percent increase? _____ %

Name:	Date: ....

Topic	*Discount, Tax and Tip*
Notes	✓ Discount = Multiply the regular price by the rate of discount ✓ Selling price = original price − discount ✓ To find tax, multiply the tax rate to the taxable amount (income, property value, etc.) ✓ To find tip, multiply the rate to the selling price.
Example	The original price of a table is $300 and the tax rate is 6%. What is the final price of the table? **Solution:** First find the tax amount. To find tax: Multiply the tax rate to the taxable amount. Tax rate is 6% or 0.06. Then: $0.06 \times 300 = 18$. The tax amount is $18. Final price is: $300 + $18 = $318

Your Turn!	1) Original price of a chair: $300 Tax: 15%, Selling price: $_____	2) Original price of a computer: $750 Discount: 20%, Selling price: $_____
	3) Original price of a printer: $250 Tax: 10%, Selling price: $_____	4) Original price of a sofa: $620 Discount: 25%, Selling price: $_____
	5) Original price of a mattress: $800 Tax: 12%, Selling price: $_____	6) Original price of a book: $150 Discount: 60%, Selling price: $_____
	7) Restaurant bill: $35.00 Tip: 20%, Final amount: $_____	8) Restaurant bill: $60.00 Tip: 25%, Final amount: $_____

Name: ....

Date: ....

Topic	*Simple Interest*
Notes	✓ Simple Interest: The charge for borrowing money or the return for lending it. To solve a simple interest problem, use this formula: Interest = principal x rate x time $\Rightarrow$ $I = p \times r \times t$
Example	Find simple interest for $3,000 investment at 5% for 4 years. **Solution:** Use Interest formula: $I = prt$ ($P = \$3,000$, r = 5% = 0.05 and $t = 4$) Then: $I = 3,000 \times 0.05 \times 4 = \$600$
Your Turn!	1) $250 at 4% for 3 years. Simple interest: $_____ 2) $3,300 at 5% for 6 years. Simple interest: $_____ 3) $720 at 2% for 5 years. Simple interest: $_____ 4) $2,200 at 8% for 4 years. Simple interest: $_____ 5) $1,800 at 3% for 2 years. Simple interest: $_____ 6) $530 at 4% for 5 years. Simple interest: $_____ 7) $7,000 at 5% for 3 months. Simple interest: $_____ 8) $880 at 5% for 9 months. Simple interest: $_____

Answers– Chapter 3

Simplifying Ratios

1) $\frac{1}{8}$
2) $\frac{5}{16}$
3) $\frac{3}{7}$

4) $\frac{7}{9}$
5) $\frac{1}{3}$
6) $\frac{3}{8}$

7) $\frac{3}{4}$
8) $\frac{5}{9}$

Proportional Ratios

1) 72
2) 40
3) 22
4) 120

5) 36
6) 70
7) 105

8) 76

Similarity and ratios

1) 24
2) 11

3) 4
4) 8

5) 10
6) 9

Percent Problems

1) 200
2) 13%
3) 1200

4) 16%
5) 300
6) 9%

7) 400
8) 5%

Percent of Increase and Decrease

1) 12.5%
2) 20%

3) 20%
4) 30%

Discount, Tax and Tip

1) $345
2) $600
3) $275

4) $465
5) $896
6) $60

7) $42
8) $75

Simple Interest

1) $30
2) $990
3) $72

4) $704
5) $108
6) $106

7) $87.50
8) $33

Chapter 4:

Algebraic Expressions

Topics that you'll practice in this chapter:

- ✓ Simplifying Variable Expressions
- ✓ Simplifying Polynomial Expressions
- ✓ The Distributive Property
- ✓ Evaluating One Variable Expressions
- ✓ Evaluating Two Variables Expressions

Name: ....

Date: ....

Topic	*Simplifying Variable Expressions*
Notes	✓ In algebra, a variable is a letter used to stand for a number. The most common letters are: $x, y, z, a, b, c, m, and\ n$. ✓ Algebraic expression is an expression contains integers, variables, and the math operations such as addition, subtraction, multiplication, division, etc. ✓ In an expression, we can combine "like" terms. (values with same variable and same power)
Example	*Simplify this expression.* $(6x + 8x + 9) =?$ **Solution:** Combine like terms. Then: $(6x + 8x + 4) = 14x + 9$ (remember you cannot combine variables and numbers.

Your Turn!	1) $5x + 2 - 2x =$	2) $4 + 7x + 3x =$
	3) $8x + 3 - 3x =$	4) $-2 - x^2 - 6x^2 =$
	5) $3 + 10x^2 + 2 =$	6) $8x^2 + 6x + 7x^2 =$
	7) $5x^2 - 12x^2 + 8x =$	8) $2x^2 - 2x - x + 5x^2 =$
	9) $4x - (12 - 30x) =$	10) $\quad 10x - (80x - 48) =$

Name: ....

Date: ....

Topic	*Simplifying Polynomial Expressions*	
Notes	✓ In mathematics, a polynomial is an expression consisting of variables and coefficients that involves only the operations of addition, subtraction, multiplication, and non–negative integer exponents of variables. $$P(x) = a_n x^n + a_{n-1} x^{n-1} + \dots + a_2 x^2 + a_1 x + a_0$$	
Example	*Simplify this expression.* $(2x^2 - x^4) - (4x^4 - x^2) =$ **Solution:** First use distributive property: → multiply $(-)$ into $(4x^4 - x^2)$ $(2x^2 - x^4) - (4x^4 - x^2) = 2x^2 - x^4 - 4x^4 + x^2$ Then combine "like" terms: $2x^2 - x^4 - 4x^4 + x^2 = 3x^2 - 5x^4$ And write in standard form: $3x^2 - 5x^4 = -5x^4 + 3x^2$	
Your Turn!	1) $(2x^3 + 5x^2) - (12x + 2x^2) =$	2) $(2x^5 + 2x^3) - (7x^3 + 6x^2) =$
	3) $(12x^4 + 4x^2) - (2x^2 - 6x^4) =$	4) $14x - 3x^2 - 2(6x^2 + 6x^3) =$
	5) $(5x^3 - 3) + 5(2x^2 - 3x^3) =$	6) $(4x^3 - 2x) - 2(4x^3 - 2x^4) =$
	7) $2(4x - 3x^3) - 3(3x^3 + 4x^2) =$	8) $(2x^2 - 2x) - (2x^3 + 5x^2) =$

| Name: .... | Date: .... |

Topic	**The Distributive Property**
Notes	✓ The distributive property (or the distributive property of multiplication over addition and subtraction) simplifies and solves expressions in the form of: $a(b + c)$ or $a(b - c)$ ✓ Distributive Property rule: $$a(b + c) = ab + ac$$
Example	*Simply.* $(5)(2x - 8)$ **Solution**: Use Distributive Property rule: $a(b + c) = ab + ac$ $$(5)(2x - 8) = (5 \times 2x) + (5) \times (-8) = 10x - 40$$

Your Turn!	1) $(-2)(4 - 3x) =$	2) $(6 - 3x)(-7)$
	3) $6(5 - 9x) =$	4) $10(3 - 5x) =$
	5) $5(6 - 5x) =$	6) $(-2)(-5x + 3) =$
	7) $(8 - 9x)(5) =$	8) $(-16x + 15)(-3) =$
	9) $(-2x + 7)(3) =$	10) $(-18x + 25)(-2) =$

Name:	Date: ....

Topic	**Evaluating One Variable Expressions**	
Notes	✓ To evaluate one variable expression, find the variable and substitute a number for that variable. ✓ Perform the arithmetic operations.	
Example	*Find the value of this expression for* $x = -3$. $-3x - 13$ **Solution:** Substitute -3 for x, then: $-3x - 13 = -3(-3) - 13 = 9 - 13 = -4$	
Your Turn!	1) $x = -3 \Rightarrow 3x + 8 =$	2) $x = 4 \Rightarrow 4(2x + 6) =$
	3) $x = -1 \Rightarrow 6x + 4 =$	4) $x = 7 \Rightarrow 6(5x + 3) =$
	5) $x = 4 \Rightarrow 5(3x + 2) =$	6) $x = 6 \Rightarrow 3(2x + 4) =$
	7) $x = 3 \Rightarrow 7(3x + 1) =$	8) $x = 8 \Rightarrow 3(3x + 7) =$
	9) $x = 9 \Rightarrow 2(x + 9) =$	10) $x = 7 \Rightarrow 2(4x + 5) =$

Name: ....

Date: ....

Topic	**Evaluating Two Variables**
Notes	✓ To evaluate an algebraic expression, substitute a number for each variable. ✓ Perform the arithmetic operations to find the value of the expression.
Example	*Evaluate this expression for* $a = 4$ *and* $b = -2$. $5a - 6b$ **Solution:** Substitute 4 for a, and -2 for b , then: $$5a - 6b = 5(4) - 6(-2) = 20 + 12 = 32$$

Your Turn!	1) $-4a + 6b$, $a = 4$, $b = 3$ _____	2) $5x + 3y$, $x = 2$, $y = -1$ _____
	3) $-5a + 3b$, $a = 2$, $b = -2$ _____	4) $3x - 4y$, $x = 6$, $y = 2$ _____
	5) $2z + 14 + 6k$, $z = 5$, $k = 3$ _____	6) $7a - (9 - 3b)$, $a = 1$, $b = 1$ _____
	7) $-6a + 3b$, $a = 4$, $b = 3$ _____	8) $-2a + b$, $a = 6$, $b = 9$ _____
	9) $8x + 2y$, $x = 4$, $y = 5$ _____	10) $z + 4 + 2k$, $z = 7$, $k = 4$ _____

Answers– Chapter 4

Simplifying Variable Expressions

1) $3x + 2$
2) $10x + 4$
3) $5x + 3$
4) $-7x^2 - 2$

5) $10x^2 + 5$
6) $15x^2 + 6x$
7) $-7x^2 + 8x$
8) $72x^2 - 3x$

9) $34x - 12$
10) $-70x - 48$

Simplifying Polynomial Expressions

1) $2x^3 + 3x^2 - 12x$
2) $2x^5 - 5x^3 - 6x^2$
3) $18x^4 + 2x^2$

4) $-12x^3 - 15x^2 + 14x$
5) $-10x^3 + 10x^2 - 3$
6) $4x^4 - 4x^3 - 2$

7) $-15x^3 - 12x^2 + 8x$
8) $2x^3 - 3x^2 - 2x$

The Distributive Property

1) $6x - 8$
2) $21x - 42$
3) $-54x + 30$
4) $-50x + 30$

5) $-25x + 30$
6) $10x - 6$
7) $-45x + 40$
8) $48x - 45$

9) $-6x + 21$
10) $36x - 50$

Evaluating One Variables

1) -1
2) 56
3) -2
4) 228

5) 70
6) 48
7) 70
8) 93

9) 36
10) 66

Evaluating Two Variables

1) 2
2) 7
3) -16
4) 10

5) 42
6) 1
7) -15
8) -3

9) 42
10) 19

Chapter 5:

Equations and Inequalities

Topics that you'll practice in this chapter:

✓ One–Step Equations

✓ Multi–Step Equations

✓ Graphing Single–Variable Inequalities

✓ One–Step Inequalities

✓ Multi-Step Inequalities

Name: ....

Date: ....

Topic	*One–Step Equations*

Notes	✓ You only need to perform one Math operation in order to solve the one-step equations.
	✓ To solve one-step equation, find the inverse (opposite) operation is being performed.
	✓ The inverse operations are:
	   - Addition and subtraction
	   - Multiplication and division

Example	*Solve this equation.* $x + 42 = 60 \Rightarrow x = ?$ **Solution:** Here, the operation is addition and its inverse operation is subtraction. To solve this equation, subtract 42 from both sides of the *equation:* $x + 42 - 42 = 60 - 42$ Then simplify: $x + 42 - 42 = 60 - 42 \Rightarrow x = 18$
Your Turn!	1) $x - 15 = 36 \Rightarrow x = $ ____ 2) $18 = 13 + x \Rightarrow x = $ ____ 3) $x - 22 = 54 \Rightarrow x = $ ____ 4) $x + 14 = 24 \Rightarrow x = $ ____ 5) $4x = 24 \Rightarrow x = $ ____ 6) $\frac{x}{6} = -3 \Rightarrow x = $ ____ 7) $99 = 11x \Rightarrow x = $ ____ 8) $\frac{x}{12} = 6 \Rightarrow x = $ ____

Name: ....

Date: ....

Topic	**Multi –Step Equations**
Notes	✓ Combine "like" terms on one side. ✓ Bring variables to one side by adding or subtracting. ✓ Simplify using the inverse of addition or subtraction. ✓ Simplify further by using the inverse of multiplication or division. ✓ Check your solution by plugging the value of the variable into the original equation.
Example	*Solve this equation for* x. $2x - 3 = 13$ **Solution:** The inverse of subtraction is addition. Add 3 to both sides of the equation. Then: $2x - 3 = 13 \Rightarrow 2x - 3 = 13 + 3$ $\Rightarrow 2x = 16$. ***Now, divide*** both sides by 2, then: $\frac{2x}{2} = \frac{16}{2} \Rightarrow x = 8$ Now, check the solution: $x = 8 \Rightarrow 2x - 3 = 13 \Rightarrow 2(8) - 3 = 13 \Rightarrow 16 - 3 = 13$ The answer $x = 8$ is correct.

Your Turn!	1) $4x - 12 = 8 \Rightarrow x =$	2) $12 - 3x = -6 + 3x \Rightarrow x =$
	3) $3(4 - 2x) = 24 \Rightarrow x =$	4) $15 + 5x = -7 - 6x \Rightarrow x =$
	5) $-2(5 + x) = 2 \Rightarrow x$	6) $12 - 2x = -3 - 5x \Rightarrow x =$
	7) $14 = -(x - 9) \Rightarrow x =$	8) $11 - 4x = -4 - 3x \Rightarrow x =$

Name: ....

Date: ....

Topic	*Graphing Single–Variable Inequalities*
Notes	✓ An inequality compares two expressions using an inequality sign. ✓ Inequality signs are: "less than" $<$, "greater than" $>$, "less than or equal to" $\leq$, and "greater than or equal to" $\geq$. ✓ To graph a single–variable inequality, find the value of the inequality on the number line. ✓ For less than ($<$) or greater than ($>$) draw open circle on the value of the variable. If there is an equal sign too, then use filled circle. ✓ Draw an arrow to the right for greater or to the left for less than.
Example	*Draw a graph for this inequality.* $x < 5$ **Solution:** Since, the variable is less than 5, then we need to find 5 in the number line and draw an open circle on it. Then, draw an arrow to the left. number line graph showing open circle at 5 with arrow pointing left
Your Turn!	1) $x < 4$ 2) $x \geq -1$ 3) $x \geq -3$ 4) $x \leq 6$ 5) $x > -6$ 6) $2 > x$ 7) $-2 \leq x$ 8) $x > 0$

Name: ....

Date: ....

Topic	*One–Step Inequalities*
Notes	✓ Inequality signs are: "less than" $<$, "greater than" $>$, "less than or equal to" $\leq$, and "greater than or equal to" $\geq$. ✓ You only need to perform one Math operation in order to solve the one-step inequalities. ✓ To solve one-step inequalities, find the inverse (opposite) operation is being performed. ✓ For dividing or multiplying both sides by negative numbers, flip the direction of the inequality sign.
Example	*Solve this inequality.* $x + 12 < 60 \Rightarrow$ _____ **Solution:** Here, the operation is addition and its inverse operation is subtraction. To solve this inequality, subtract 12 from both sides of the ***inequality:*** $x + 12 - 12 < 60 - 12$ Then simplify: $x < 48$
Your Turn!	1) $4x < -8 \Rightarrow$ _____ 2) $x + 6 > 28 \Rightarrow$ _____ 3) $-3x \geq 36 \Rightarrow$ _____ 4) $x - 16 \leq 4 \Rightarrow$ _____ 5) $\frac{x}{2} \geq -9 \Rightarrow$ _____ 6) $48 < 6x \Rightarrow$ _____ 7) $77 \leq 11x \Rightarrow$ _____ 8) $\frac{x}{4} > 9 \Rightarrow$ _____

Name:	Date: ....

Topic	*Multi −Step Inequalities*
Notes	✓ Isolate the variable. ✓ Simplify using the inverse of addition or subtraction. ✓ Simplify further by using the inverse of multiplication or division. ✓ For dividing or multiplying both sides by negative numbers, flip the direction of the inequality sign.
Example	*Solve this inequality.* $3x + 12 \leq 21$ **Solution:** First subtract 12 from both sides: $3x + 12 - 12 \leq 21 - 12$ Then simplify: $3x + 12 - 12 \leq 21 - 12 \rightarrow 3x \leq 9$ Now divide both sides by 3: $\frac{3x}{3} \leq \frac{9}{3} \rightarrow x \leq 3$
Your Turn!	1) $5x + 6 < 36 \rightarrow$ _____ 2) $2x - 8 \leq 6 \rightarrow$ _____ 3) $2x - 5 \leq 17 \rightarrow$ _____ 4) $14 - 7x \geq -7 \rightarrow$ _____ 5) $18 - 6x \geq -6 \rightarrow$ _____ 6) $2x - 18 \leq 16 \rightarrow$ _____ 7) $8 + 4x < 44 \rightarrow$ _____ 8) $5 - 4x < 17 \rightarrow$ _____

Answers– Chapter 5

One–Step Equations

1) 51
2) 5
3) 76

4) 10
5) 6
6) −18

7) 9
8) 72

Multi–Step Equations

1) 5
2) 3
3) −2

4) −2
5) −6
6) −5

7) −5
8) 15

Graphing Single–Variable Inequalities

1) $x < 4$ 	2) $x \geq -1$ 
3) $x \geq -3$	4) $x \leq 6$ 
5) $x > -6$	6) $2 > x$ 
7) $-2 \leq x$	8) $x > 0$ 

One–Step Inequalities

1) $x < -2$
2) $x > 22$
3) $x \leq -12$
4) $x \leq 20$

5) $x \geq -18$
6) $8 < x$
7) $7 \leq x$
8) $x > 36$

Multi-Step Inequalities

1) $x < 6$
2) $x \leq 7$
3) $x \leq 11$
4) $x \leq 3$

5) $x \leq 4$
6) $x \leq 17$
7) $x < 9$
8) $x > -3$

Chapter 6:

Exponents and Radicals

Topics that you'll practice in this chapter:

✓ Multiplication Property of Exponents

✓ Zero and Negative Exponents

✓ Division Property of Exponents

✓ Powers of Products and Quotients

✓ Negative Exponents and Negative Bases

✓ Scientific Notation

✓ Radicals

Name: ....

Date: ....

Topic	**Multiplication Property of Exponents**
Notes	✓ Exponents are shorthand for repeated multiplication of the same number by itself. For example, instead of 2×2, we can write 2^2. For $3 \times 3 \times 3 \times 3$, we can write 3^4 ✓ In algebra, a variable is a letter used to stand for a number. The most common letters are: $x, y, z, a, b, c, m, and\ n$. ✓ Exponent's rules: $x^a \times x^b = x^{a+b}$, $\frac{x^a}{x^b} = x^{a-b}$ $\quad (x^a)^b = x^{a \times b} \qquad (xy)^a = x^a \times y^a \qquad (\frac{a}{b})^c = \frac{a^c}{b^c}$
Example	*Multiply.* $4x^3 \times 2x^2$ **Solution:** Use Exponent's rules: $x^a \times x^b = x^{a+b} \rightarrow x^3 \times x^2 = x^{3+2} = x^5$ Then: $4x^3 \times 2x^2 = 8x^5$
Your Turn!	1) $x^2 \times 3x =$ 2) $5x^4 \times x^2 =$ 3) $3x^2 \times 4x^5 =$ 4) $3x^2 \times 6xy =$ 5) $3x^5y \times 5x^2y^3 =$ 6) $3x^2y^2 \times 5x^2y^8 =$ 7) $5x^2y \times 5x^2y^7 =$ 8) $6x^6 \times 4x^9y^4 =$ 9) $8x^2y^5 \times 7x^5y^3 =$ 10) $12x^6x^2 \times 3xy^5 =$

Name: ....

Date: ....

Topic	*Zero and Negative Exponents*
Notes	✓ A negative exponent is the reciprocal of that number with a positive exponent. $(3)^{-2} = \frac{1}{3^2}$ ✓ Zero-Exponent Rule: $a^0 = 1$, this means that anything raised to the zero power is 1. For example: $(28x^2y)^0 = 1$
Example	*Evaluate.* $\left(\frac{1}{3}\right)^{-2} =$ **Solution:** Use negative exponent's rule: $\left(\frac{1}{x^a}\right)^{-2} = (x^a)^2 \rightarrow \left(\frac{1}{3}\right)^{-2} = (3)^2 =$ Then: $(3)^2 = 9$

Your Turn!	1) $2^{-3} =$	2) $3^{-3} =$
	3) $7^{-3} =$	4) $1^{-3} =$
	5) $8^{-3} =$	6) $4^{-4} =$
	7) $10^{-3} =$	8) $7^{-4} =$
	9) $\left(\frac{1}{8}\right)^{-1} =$	10) $\left(\frac{1}{5}\right)^{-2} =$

Name:	Date: ....

Topic	**Division Property of Exponents**
Notes	✓ For division of exponents use these formulas: $\frac{x^a}{x^b} = x^{a-b}$, $x \neq 0$ $\frac{x^a}{x^b} = \frac{1}{x^{b-a}}$, $x \neq 0$, $\frac{1}{x^b} = x^{-b}$
Example	*Simplify.* $\frac{6x^3y}{36x^2y^3}$ **Solution:** First cancel the common factor: $6 \rightarrow \frac{6x^3y}{36x^2y^3} = \frac{x^3y}{6x^2y^3}$ Use Exponent's rules: $\frac{x^a}{x^b} = x^{a-b} \rightarrow \frac{x^3}{x^2} = x^{3-2} = x^1 = x$ Then: $\frac{6x^3y}{36x^2y^3} = \frac{xy}{9y^3} \rightarrow$ now cancel the common factor: $y \rightarrow \frac{xy}{6y^3} = \frac{x}{6y^2}$
Your Turn!	1) $\frac{3^7}{3^2} =$ 2) $\frac{5x}{10x^3} =$ 3) $\frac{3x^3}{2x^5} =$ 4) $\frac{12x^3}{14x^6} =$ 5) $\frac{12x^3}{9y^8} =$ 6) $\frac{25xy^4}{5x^6y^2} =$ 7) $\frac{2x^4y^5}{7xy^2} =$ 8) $\frac{16x^2y^8}{4x^3} =$ 9) $\frac{12x^4}{15x^7y^9} =$ 10) $\frac{12yx^4}{10yx^8} =$

Name: ....

Date: ....

Topic	**Powers of Products and Quotients**
Notes	For any nonzero numbers a and b and any integer x, $$(ab)^x = a^x \times b^x, \left(\frac{a}{b}\right)^c = \frac{a^c}{b^c}$$
Example	*Simplify.* $\left(\frac{2x^3}{x}\right)^2$ **Solution:** First cancel the common factor: $x \to \left(\frac{2x^3}{x}\right)^2 = (2x^2)^2$ Use Exponent's rules: $(ab)^x = a^x \times b^x$ Then: $(2x^2)^2 = (2)^2(x^2)^2 = 4x^4$
Your Turn!	1) $(4x^3 x^3)^2 =$ 2) $(3x^3 \times 5x)^2 =$ 3) $(10x^{11}y^3)^2 =$ 4) $(9x^7 y^5)^2 =$ 5) $(4x^4 y^6)^3 =$ 6) $(3x \times 4y^3)^2 =$ 7) $\left(\frac{5x}{x^2}\right)^2 =$ 8) $\left(\frac{x^4 y^4}{x^2 y^2}\right)^3 =$ 9) $\left(\frac{25x}{5x^6}\right)^2 =$ 10) $\left(\frac{x^8}{x^6 y^2}\right)^2 =$

Name: ....

Date: ....

Topic	*Negative Exponents and Negative Bases*
Notes	✓ Make the power positive. A negative exponent is the reciprocal of that number with a positive exponent. ✓ The parenthesis is important! 5^{-2} is not the same as $(-5)^{-2}$ $(-5)^{-2} = -\frac{1}{5^2}$ and $(-5)^{-2} = +\frac{1}{5^2}$
Example	*Simplify.* $(-\frac{3x}{4yz})^{-2} =$ **Solution:** Use negative exponent's rule: $(\frac{x^a}{x^b})^{-2} = (\frac{x^b}{x^a})^2 \rightarrow (-\frac{3x}{4yz})^{-3} = (-\frac{4yz}{3x})^3$ Now use exponent's rule: $(\frac{a}{b})^c = \frac{a^c}{b^c} \rightarrow (-\frac{4yz}{3x})^3 = \frac{4^3 y^3 z^3}{3^3 x^3} = \frac{64 y^3 z^3}{27 x^3}$
Your Turn!	1) $-5x^{-2}y^{-3} =$ 3) $14a^{-6}b^{-7} =$ 5) $-\frac{25}{x^{-6}} =$ 7) $\frac{7ab}{a^{-3}b^{-1}} =$ 9) $\frac{4ab^{-2}}{-3c^{-2}} =$ 2) $20x^{-4}y^{-1} =$ 4) $-12x^2 y^{-3} =$ 6) $\frac{7b}{-9c^{-4}} =$ 8) $-\frac{5n^{-2}}{10p^{-3}} = -$ 10) $(\frac{3a}{2c})^{-2} =$

Name:	Date: ....

Topic	*Scientific Notation*	
Notes	✓ It is used to write very big or very small numbers in decimal form. ✓ In scientific notation all numbers are written in the form of: $$m \times 10^n$$ <table><tr><td>**Decimal notation**</td><td>**Scientific notation**</td></tr><tr><td>3</td><td>3×10^0</td></tr><tr><td>$-45{,}000$</td><td>-4.5×10^4</td></tr><tr><td>0.3</td><td>3×10^{-1}</td></tr><tr><td>2,122.456</td><td>2.122456×10^3</td></tr></table>	
Example	*Write* 0.00054 *in scientific notation.* **Solution:** First, move the decimal point to the right so that you have a number that is between 1 and 10. Then: $m = 5.4$ Now, determine how many places the decimal moved in step 1 by the power of 10. Then: $10^{-4} \rightarrow$ When the decimal moved to the right, the exponent is negative. Then: $0.00054 = 5.4 \times 10^{-4}$	
Your Turn!	1) $0.000325 =$	2) $0.000023 =$
	3) $52{,}000{,}000 =$	4) $21{,}000 =$
	5) $3 \times 10^{-1} =$	6) $5 \times 10^{-2} =$
	7) $1.2 \times 10^3 =$	8) $2 \times 10^{-4} =$

Name:	Date: ....

Topic	*Radicals*
Notes	✓ If n is a positive integer and x is a real number, then: $\sqrt[n]{x} = x^{\frac{1}{n}}$, $\sqrt[n]{xy} = x^{\frac{1}{n}} \times y^{\frac{1}{n}}$, $\sqrt[n]{\frac{x}{y}} = \frac{x^{\frac{1}{n}}}{y^{\frac{1}{n}}}$, and $\sqrt[n]{x} \times \sqrt[n]{y} = \sqrt[n]{xy}$ ✓ A square root of x is a number r whose square is: $r^2 = x$ (r is a square root of $\boldsymbol{x}$. ✓ To add and subtract radicals, we need to have the same values under the radical. For example: $\sqrt{3} + \sqrt{3} = 2\sqrt{3}$, $3\sqrt{5} - \sqrt{5} = 2\sqrt{5}$
Example	*Evaluate.* $\sqrt{32} + \sqrt{8} =$ **Solution:** Since we do not have the same values under the radical, we cannot add these two radicals. But we can simplify each radical. $\sqrt{32} = \sqrt{16} \times \sqrt{2} = 4\sqrt{2}$ and $\sqrt{8} = \sqrt{4} \times \sqrt{2} = 2\sqrt{2}$ Now, we have the same values under the radical. Then: $$\sqrt{32} + \sqrt{8} = 4\sqrt{2} + 2\sqrt{2} = 6\sqrt{2}$$
Your Turn!	1) $\sqrt{9} \times \sqrt{9} =$ 2) $\sqrt{8} \times \sqrt{2} =$ 3) $\sqrt{3} \times \sqrt{27} =$ 4) $\sqrt{32} \div \sqrt{2} =$ 5) $\sqrt{2} + \sqrt{8} =$ 6) $\sqrt{27} - \sqrt{3} =$ 7) $4\sqrt{5} - 2\sqrt{5} =$ 8) $3\sqrt{3} \times 2\sqrt{3} =$

Answers– Chapter 6

Multiplication Property of Exponents

1) $3x^3$
2) $5x^6$
3) $12x^7$
4) $18x^3y$
5) $15x^7y^4$

6) $15x^4y^{10}$
7) $25x^4y^8$
8) $24x^{15}y^4$
9) $56x^7y^8$
10) $36x^9y^5$

Zero and Negative Exponents

1) $\frac{1}{8}$
2) $\frac{1}{27}$
3) $\frac{1}{343}$
4) 1
5) $\frac{1}{512}$

6) $\frac{1}{256}$
7) $\frac{1}{1,000}$
8) $\frac{1}{2,401}$
9) 8
10) 25

Division Property of Exponents

1) 3^5
2) $\frac{1}{2x^2}$
3) $\frac{3}{2x^2}$
4) $\frac{6}{7x^3}$
5) $\frac{4x^3}{3y^8}$

6) $\frac{5y^2}{x^5}$
7) $\frac{2x^3y^3}{7}$
8) $\frac{4y^8}{x}$
9) $\frac{4}{5x^3y^9}$
10) $\frac{6y^6}{5x^4}$

Powers of Products and Quotients

1) $16x^{12}$
2) $225x^8$
3) $100x^{22}y^6$
4) $81x^{14}y^{10}$
5) $64 x^{12}y^{18}$
6) $144x^2y^6$

7) $\frac{25}{x^2}$
8) x^6y^6
9) $\frac{25}{x^{10}}$
10) $\frac{x^4}{y^4}$

Negative Exponents and Negative Bases

1) $-\dfrac{5}{x^2 y^3}$

2) $\dfrac{20}{x^4 y}$

3) $\dfrac{14}{a^6 b^7}$

4) $-\dfrac{12^2}{y^3}$

5) $-25x^6$

6) $-\dfrac{7bc^4}{9}$

7) $7a^4 b^2$

8) $-\dfrac{p^3}{2n^2}$

9) $-\dfrac{4ac^2}{3b^2}$

10) $\dfrac{4c^2}{9a^2}$

Scientific Notation

1) 3.25×10^{-4}

2) 2.3×10^{-5}

3) 5.2×10^7

4) 2.1×10^4

5) 0.3

6) 0.05

7) $1,200$

8) 0.0002

Radicals

1) 9

2) 4

3) 9

4) 4

5) $3\sqrt{2}$

6) $2\sqrt{3}$

7) $2\sqrt{5}$

8) 18

Chapter 7:

Geometry and Solid Figures

Topics that you'll practice in this chapter:

- ✓ The Pythagorean Theorem
- ✓ Circles
- ✓ Rectangular Prism
- ✓ Cylinder

Name: ....

Date: ....

Topic	*The Pythagorean Theorem*
Notes	✓ In any right triangle: $a^2 + b^2 = c^2$
Example	Right triangle ABC (not shown) has two legs of lengths 18 cm (AB) and 24 cm (AC). What is the length of the third side (BC)? **Solution:** Use Pythagorean Theorem: $a^2 + b^2 = c^2$ Then: $a^2 + b^2 = c^2 \rightarrow 18^2 + 24^2 = c^2 \rightarrow 324 + 576 = c^2$ $c^2 = 900 \rightarrow c = \sqrt{900} = 30\ cm$
Your Turn!	1) _____ 2) _____ 3) _____ 4) _____

Name: ....

Date: ....

Topic	*Triangles*
Notes	✓ In any triangle the sum of all angles is 180 degrees. ✓ Area of a triangle = $\frac{1}{2}(base \times height)$
Example	What is the area of the following triangle? **Solution:** Use the area formula: Area $= \frac{1}{2}(base \times height)$ $base = 16$ and $height = 6$ Area $= \frac{1}{2}(16 \times 6) = \frac{96}{2} = 48$
Your Turn!	1) _____ 24, 10 2) _____ 18, 28 3) _____ 20, 30 4) _____ 32, 46

Name: ....

Date: ....

Topic	Polygons
Notes	Perimeter of a square $= 4 \times side = 4s$ Perimeter of a rectangle $= 2(width + length)$ Perimeter of trapezoid $= a + b + c + d$ Perimeter of a regular hexagon $= 6a$ Perimeter of a parallelogram $= 2(l + w)$

Example	*Find the perimeter of following regular hexagon.* **Solution:** Since the hexagon is regular, all sides are equal. Then: Perimeter of Hexagon $= 6 \times (one\ side)$ Perimeter of Hexagon $= 6 \times (one\ side) = 6 \times 9 = 54\ m$

Your Turn!	1) *(rectangle)* _____ 9 in 15 in	2) _____ 8 m 10 m 10 m 14 m
	3) *(regular hexagon)*_____ 5 m	4) *(parallelogram)*_____ 10 in 16 in

Name: ....

Date: ....

Topic	*Cubes*
Notes	✓ A cube is a three-dimensional solid object bounded by six square sides. ✓ Volume is the measure of the amount of space inside of a solid figure, like a cube, ball, cylinder or pyramid. ✓ Volume of a cube $= (one\ side)^3$ ✓ surface area of cube $= 6 \times (one\ side)^2$
Example	Find the volume and surface area of the following cube. 15 *cm* **Solution:** Use volume formula: $volume = (one\ side)^3$ Then: $volume = (one\ side)^3 = (15)^3 = 3,375\ cm^3$ Use surface area formula: $surface\ area\ of\ cube$: $6(one\ side)^2 = 6(15)^2 = 6(225) = 1,350\ cm^2$
Your Turn!	**Find the volume of each cube.** 1) _____ 11 *in* 2) _____ 13 *ft* 3) _____ 14 *cm* 4) _____ 30 *m*

Name: ....   Date: ....

Topic	*Trapezoids*
Notes	✓ A quadrilateral with at least one pair of parallel sides is a trapezoid. ✓ Area of a trapezoid $= \frac{1}{2}h(b_1 + b_2)$
Example	Calculate the area of the trapezoid. **Solution:** Use area formula: $A = \frac{1}{2}h(b_1 + b_2)$ $b_1 = 8\ cm$, $b_2 = 12\ cm$ and $h = 14\ cm$ Then: $A = \frac{1}{2}(14)(12 + 8) = 7(20) = 140\ cm^2$
Your Turn!	1) _____ 5 cm 4 cm 9 cm 2) _____ 8 m 10 m 12 m 3) _____ 7 ft 6 ft 15 ft 4) _____ 10 cm 8 cm 14 cm

Name: ………………………………………….

Date: ………………………………………………..

Topic	*Circles*
Notes	✓ In a circle, variable r is usually used for the radius and d for diameter and π is about 3.14. ✓ $Area\ of\ a\ circle = \pi r^2$ ✓ $Circumference\ of\ a\ circle = 2\pi r$ r

Example	Find the area of the circle.
	    Solution:
	    Use area formula: $Area = \pi r^2$
	    $r = 2\ in \rightarrow Area = \pi(2)^2 = 4\pi, \pi = 3.14$
	    $Then:\ Area = 4 \times 3.14 = 12.56\ in^2$
	
	$2\ in$

Your Turn!	**Find the area of each circle.** $(\pi = 3.14)$ 1) _____ 2) _____ 6 cm 10 in **Find the Circumference of each circle.** $(\pi = 3.14)$ 3) _____ 4) _____ 8 cm 6 m

Name: ....

Date: ....

Topic	*Rectangular Prisms*
Notes	✓ A solid 3-dimensional object which has six rectangular faces. ✓ Volume of a Rectangular prism = **Length × Width × Height** $Volume = l \times w \times h$ $Surface\ area = 2(wh + lw + lh)$
Example	Find the volume and surface area of rectangular prism. **Solution:** Use volume formula: $Volume = l \times w \times h$ Then: $Volume = 4 \times 2 \times 6 = 48\ m^3$ Use surface area formula: $Surface\ area = 2(wh + lw + lh)$ Then: $Surface\ area = 2\big((2 \times 6) + (4 \times 2) + (4 \times 6)\big)$ $= 2(12 + 8 + 24) = 2(44) = 88\ m^2$

Find the surface area of each Rectangular Prism.

Your Turn!

1) _____

6 ft, 10 ft, 4 ft

2) _____

8 cm, 16 cm, 6 cm

3) _____

12 m, 18 m, 10 m

4) _____

20 in, 15 in, 12 in

Name: …………………………………………..   Date: ……………………………………………….

Topic	*Cylinder*
Notes	✓ A cylinder is a solid geometric figure with straight parallel sides and a circular or oval cross section. ✓ *Volume of Cylinder Formula* $= \pi(radius)^2 \times height$ $\pi = 3.14$ ✓ *Surface area of a cylinder* $= 2\pi r^2 + 2\pi rh$ *heigh* *radius*
Example	*Find the volume and Surface area of the follow Cylinder.* **Solution:** Use volume formula: $Volume = \pi(radius)^2 \times height$ Then: $Volume = \pi(3)^2 \times 12 = 9\pi \times 12 = 108\pi$ $\pi = 3.14$ **then:** $Volume = 108\pi = 339.12\ cm^3$ Use surface area formula: $Surface\ area = 2\pi r^2 + 2\pi rh$ **Then:** $2\pi(3)^2 + 2\pi(3)(12) = 2\pi(9) + 2\pi(36) = 18\pi + 72\pi = 90\pi$ $\pi = 3.14$ **Then:** $Surface\ area = 90 \times 3.14 = 282.6\ cm^2$ *12 cm* *3 cm*
Your Turn!	**Find the volume of each Cylinder.** $(\pi = 3.14)$ 1) _____ *10 in* *2 in* 2) _____ *14 m* *5 m* **Find the Surface area of each Cylinder.** $(\pi = 3.14)$ 3) _____ *15 ft* *9 ft* 4) _____ *20 cm* *12 cm*

Answers– Chapter 7

The Pythagorean Theorem

1) 17
2) 30

3) 12
4) 9

Triangles

1) 120
2) 252

3) 300
4) 736

Polygons

1) 48 in
2) 42 m

3) 30 m
4) 52 in

Cubes

1) 1,331 in^3
2) 2,197 ft^3

3) 2,744 cm^3
4) 27,000 m^3

Trapezoids

1) 28 cm^2
2) 100 m^2

3) 66 ft^2
4) 96 cm^2

Circle

1) 113.04 cm^2
2) 314 in^2

3) 50.24 cm
4) 37.68 m

Rectangular Prism

1) 248 ft^2
2) 544 cm^2

3) 1,032 m^2
4) 1,440 in^2

Cylinder

1) 125.6 in^3
2) 1,099 m^3

3) 1,356.48 ft^2
4) 2,411.52 cm^2

Chapter 8:

Statistics and Probability

Topics that you'll practice in this chapter:

- ✓ Mean, Median, Mode, and Range of the Given Data
- ✓ Pie Graph
- ✓ Probability Problems

Name: ....

Date: ....

Topic	*Mean, Median, Mode, and Range of the Given Data*
Notes	✔ Mean: $\dfrac{sum\ of\ the\ data}{total\ number\ of\ data\ entires}$ ✔ Mode: value in the list that appears most often. ✔ Median: is the middle number of a group of numbers that have been arranged in order by size. ✔ Range: the difference of largest value and smallest value in the list.
Example	*Find the mode and median of these numbers?* $16, 10, 6, 3, 1, 16, 2, 4$ **Solution:** Mode: value in the list that appears most often. Number 16 is the value in the list that appears most often (there are two number 16). To find median, write the numbers in order: $1, 2, 3, 4, 6, 10, 16, 16$ Number 4 and 6 are in the middle. Find their average: $\dfrac{4+6}{2} = \dfrac{10}{2} = 5$ The median is 5.
Your Turn!	1) $3, 2, 4, 8, 3, 10$ Mode: _____ Range: _____ Mean: _____ Median: _____ 2) $6, 3, 2, 9, 5, 7, 2, 14$ Mode: _____ Range: _____ Mean: _____ Median: _____ 3) $5, 4, 3, 2, 9, 5, 6, 8, 12$ Mode: _____ Range: _____ Mean: _____ Median: _____ 4) $12, 6, 8, 6, 9, 6, 4, 13$ Mode: _____ Range: _____ Mean: _____ Median: _____

Name: .... Date: ....

Topic	*Pie Graph*
Notes	✓ A Pie Chart is a circle chart divided into sectors, each sector represents the relative size of each value.
Example	A library has 460 books that include Mathematics, Physics, Chemistry, English and History. Use following graph to answer the question. **What is the number of Physics books?** **Solution:** Number of total books $= 460$ Percent of Physics books $= 25\% = 0.25$ Then, umber of Physics books: $$0.25 \times 460 = 115$$
Your Turn!	The circle graph below shows all Mr. Smith's expenses for last month. Mr. Smith spent $440 for clothes last month. Mr. Smith's last month expenses
	1) How much did Mr. Smith spend for his Books last month? _____ 2) How much did Mr. Smith spend for Bills last month? _____ 3) How much did Mr. Smith spend for his foods last month? _____

Name: .... **Date:** ....

Topic	*Probability Problems*
Notes	✓ Probability is the likelihood of something happening in the future. It is expressed as a number between zero (can never happen) to 1 (will always happen). ✓ Probability can be expressed as a fraction, a decimal, or a percent. ✓ Probability formula: $Probability = \frac{number\ of\ desired\ outcomes}{number\ of\ total\ outcomes}$
Example	If there are 3 green balls, 4 red balls, and 10 blue balls in a basket, what is the probability that Jason will pick out a red ball from the basket? **Solution:** There are 4 red ball and 17 are total number of balls. Therefore, probability that Jason will pick out a red ball from the basket is 4 out of 17 or $\frac{4}{3+4+10} = \frac{4}{17}$
Your Turn!	1) A number is chosen at random from 1 to 20. Find the probability of selecting a prime number. (A prime number is a whole number that is only divisible by itself and 1) _____ 2) There are only red and blue cards in a box. The probability of choosing a red card in the box at random is one third. If there are 24 blue cards, how many cards are in the box? _____ 3) A die is rolled, what is the probability that an even number is obtained? _____

Answers– Chapter 8

Mean, Median, Mode, and Range of the Given Data

1) Mode: 3	Mean:5	Range: 8	Median: 3.5
2) Mode: 2	Mean:6	Range: 12	Median: 5.5
3) Mode: 5	Mean:6	Range: 10	Median: 5
4) Mode: 6	Mean:8	Range: 9	Median: 7

Pie Graph

1) $308
2) $396
3) $550

Probability Problems

1) $\frac{8}{20} = \frac{2}{5}$

2) 36

3) $\frac{1}{2}$

STAAR Test Review

The State of Texas Assessments of Academic Readiness (STAAR) is developed under the supervision of the Texas Education Agency and is taken by all public school students in Texas, grades 3–12. The tests measure the progress of students from 3rd grade to 8th grade, as well as high school. STAAR is the state's testing program and is based on state curriculum standards in core subjects including:

- o Reading,
- o Writing,
- o Mathematics,
- o Science,
- o Social Studies

In high school, students take end-of-course STAAR exams in five high school subjects:

- o Algebra I,
- o Biology,
- o English I,
- o English II,
- o U.S. History.

Students take STAAR tests in the spring. The number of tests a student takes each year will depend on what grade he or she is in. Most students will have two to four testing days during a school year.

In this book, there are two complete Grade 7 STAAR Math Tests. Take these tests to see what score you'll be able to receive on a real STAAR Math test.

Good luck!

Time to refine your skill with a practice examination

Take a practice STAAR Math Test to simulate the test day experience. After you've finished, score your test using the answer key.

Before You Start

- You'll need a pencil and a calculator to take the test.
- There are two types of questions:

  Multiple choice questions: for each of these questions, there are four or more possible answers. Choose which one is best.

  Grid-ins questions: for these questions, write your answer in the box provided.
- It's okay to guess. You won't lose any points if you're wrong.
- The STAAR Mathematics test contains a formula sheet, which displays formulas relating to geometric measurement and certain algebra concepts. Formulas are provided to test-takers so that they may focus on application, rather than the memorization, of formulas.
- After you've finished the test, review the answer key to see where you went wrong and what areas you need to improve.

You can use a calculator for the STAAR Grade 7 Math Test.

Good luck!

STAAR Mathematics

Practice Test 1

2020-2021

Grade 7

Total number of questions: 40

Total time to complete the test: No time limit

You may use a calculator on this practice test.

STAAR Grade 7 Mathematics Formula Sheet

LINEAR EQUATIONS

Slope – intercept form	$y = mx + b$
Direct Variation	$y = kx$
Slope of a Line	$m = \dfrac{y_2 - y_1}{x_2 - x_1}$

CIRCUMFERENCE

Circle	$C = 2\pi r$ or $C = \pi d$

AREA

Triangle	$A = \dfrac{1}{2}bh$
Parallelogram	$A = bh$
Trapezoid	$A = \dfrac{1}{2}h(b_1 + b_2)$
Circle	$A = \pi r^2$

SURFACE AREA

	Lateral	Total
Prism	$S = Ph$	$S = Ph + 2B$
Cylinder	$S = 2\pi rh$	$S = 2\pi rh + 2\pi r^2$

VOLUME

Prism or Cylinder	$V = Bh$
Pyramid or Cone	$V = \dfrac{1}{3}Bh$
Sphere	$V = \dfrac{4}{3}\pi r^3$

ADDITIONAL INFORMATION

Pythagorean theorem	$a^2 + b^2 = c^2$
Simple interest	$I = prt$
Compound Interest	$A = p(1 + r)^t$

1) What is the slope of a line that is parallel to the line with equation of $2x - y = 12$?
   A. -2
   B. 2
   C. 4
   D. 12

2) What is the value of the expression $5(x - 2y) + (2 - x)^2$ when $x = 3$ and $y = -2$?
   A. -4
   B. 20
   C. 36
   D. 50

3) The mean of 50 test scores was calculated as 88. But, it turned out that one of the scores was misread as 94 but it was 69. What is the correct mean of the data?
   A. 85
   B. 87
   C. 87.5
   D. 88.5

4) The width of a box is one third of its length. The height of the box is one third of its width. If the length of the box is 27 cm, what is the volume of the box?
   A. $81 \ cm^3$
   B. $162 \ cm^3$
   C. $243 \ cm^3$
   D. $729 \ cm^3$

5) In five successive hours, a car travels 40 km, 45 km, 50 km, 35 km and 55 km. In the next five hours, it travels with an average speed of 50 km per hour. Find the total distance the car traveled in 10 hours.
   A. $425 \ km$
   B. $450 \ km$
   C. $475 \ km$
   D. $500 \ km$

6) The ratio of boys to girls in a school is 2: 3. If there are 600 students in a school, how many boys are in the school.

   Write your answer in the box below.

   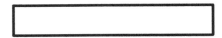

7) The perimeter of the trapezoid below is 54 cm. What is its area?

   Write your answer in the box below.

   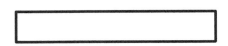

   18

   12 cm   14 cm

8) In 1999, the average worker's income increased $2,000 per year starting from $24,000 annual salary. Which equation represents income greater than average? (I = income, x = number of years after 1999)
   A. $I > 2000\,x + 24000$
   B. $I > -2000\,x + 24000$
   C. $I < -2000\,x + 24000$
   D. $I < 2000\,x - 24000$

9) Which of the following graphs represents the compound inequality $-2 \le 2x - 4 < 8$?

   A.
   -8 -6 -4 -2 0 2 4 6 8

   B.
   -8 -6 -4 -2 0 2 4 6 8

   C.
   -8 -6 -4 -2 0 2 4 6 8

   D.
   -8 -6 -4 -2 0 2 4 6 8

10) A football team had $20,000 to spend on supplies. The team spent $14,000 on new balls. New sport shoes cost $120 each. Which of the following inequalities represent how many new shoes the team can purchase?

A. $120x + 14,000 \leq 20,000$
B. $120x + 14,000 \geq 20,000$
C. $14,000x + 12,0 \leq 20,000$
D. $14,000x + 12,0 \geq 20,000$

11) Two dice are thrown simultaneously, what is the probability of getting a sum of 6 or 9?

A. $\frac{1}{3}$
B. $\frac{1}{4}$
C. $\frac{1}{6}$
D. $\frac{1}{12}$

12) A swimming pool holds 2,000 cubic feet of water. The swimming pool is 25 feet long and 10 feet wide. How deep is the swimming pool?
Write your answer in the box below.

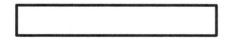

13) The height of a scale model of a building in which 3 inches represents 45 feet is 1.5 feet. What is the height of the building?

A. $270\ feet$
B. $300\ feet$
C. $330\ feet$
D. $480\ feet$

14) A bank is offering 4.5% simple interest on a savings account. If you deposit $8,000, how much interest will you earn in five years?

A. $360
B. $720
C. $1,800
D. $3,600

15) A card is drawn at random from a standard 52–card deck, what is the probability that the card is of Clubs? (The deck includes 13 of each suit clubs, diamonds, hearts, and spades)

   A. $\dfrac{1}{3}$

   B. $\dfrac{1}{4}$

   C. $\dfrac{1}{6}$

   D. $\dfrac{1}{52}$

16) How long does a 420–miles trip take moving at 50 miles per hour (mph)?

   A. *4 hours*

   B. *6 hours and 24 minutes*

   C. *8 hours and 24 minutes*

   D. *8 hours and 30 minutes*

17) 11 yards 6 feet and 4 inches equals to how many inches?

   A. 388

   B. 468

   C. 472

   D. 476

18) A shirt costing $200 is discounted 15%. After a month, the shirt is discounted another 15%. Which of the following expressions can be used to find the selling price of the shirt?

   A. $(200)(0.70)$

   B. $(200) - 200(0.30)$

   C. $(200)(0.15) - (200)(0.15)$

   D. $(200)(0.85)(0.85)$

19) Which of the following points lies on the line $2x + 4y = 10$

   A. $(2, 1)$

   B. $(-1, 3)$

   C. $(-2, 2)$

   D. $(2, 2)$

20) $5 + 8 \times (-2) - [4 + 22 \times 5] \div 6 = ?$

Write your answer in the box below.

21) The price of a car was $20,000 in 2014, $16,000 in 2015 and $12,800 in 2016. What is the rate of depreciation of the price of car per year?
   A. 15%
   B. 20%
   C. 25%
   D. 30%

22) What is the equivalent temperature of $104°F$ in Celsius?
   $$C = \frac{5}{9}(F - 32)$$
   A. 32
   B. 40
   C. 48
   D. 68

23) The square of a number is $\frac{25}{64}$. What is the cube of that number?
   A. $\frac{5}{8}$
   B. $\frac{25}{254}$
   C. $\frac{125}{512}$
   D. $\frac{125}{64}$

24) What is the surface area of the cylinder below?
   A. 48π
   B. 57π
   C. 66π
   D. 288π

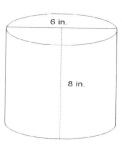
6 in.
8 in.

25) What is the value of x in the following equation?

$$\frac{2}{3}x + \frac{1}{6} = \frac{1}{3}$$

A. 6
B. $\frac{1}{2}$
C. $\frac{1}{3}$
D. $\frac{1}{4}$

26) The average of five numbers is 24. If a sixth number 42 is added, then, what is the new average?
A. 25
B. 26
C. 27
D. 28

27) Anita's trick–or–treat bag contains 12 pieces of chocolate, 18 suckers, 18 pieces of gum, 24 pieces of licorice. If she randomly pulls a piece of candy from her bag, what is the probability of her pulling out a piece of sucker?
A. $\frac{1}{3}$
B. $\frac{1}{4}$
C. $\frac{1}{6}$
D. $\frac{1}{12}$

28) Which of the following shows the numbers from least to greatest?

$$\frac{2}{3}, 0.68, 67\%, \frac{4}{5}$$

A. $67\%, 0.68, \frac{2}{3}, \frac{4}{5}$
B. $67\%, 0.68, \frac{4}{5}, \frac{2}{3}$
C. $0.68, 67\%, \frac{2}{3}, \frac{4}{5}$
D. $\frac{2}{3}, 67\%, 0.68, \frac{4}{5}$

29) Mr. Carlos family are choosing a menu for their reception. They have 3 choices of appetizers, 5 choices of entrees, 4 choices of cake. How many different menu combinations are possible for them to choose?
   A. 12
   B. 32
   C. 60
   D. 120

30) Four one – foot rulers can be split among how many users to leave each with $\frac{1}{6}$ of a ruler?
   A. 4
   B. 6
   C. 12
   D. 24

31) What is the area of a square whose diagonal is 8?
   A. 16
   B. 32
   C. 36
   D. 64

32) The ratio of boys and girls in a class is 4: 7. If there are 44 students in the class, how many more boys should be enrolled to make the ratio 1: 1?
   A. 8
   B. 10
   C. 12
   D. 14

33) What is the area of the shaded region?
   A. 31 ft
   B. 40 ft
   C. 64 ft
   D. 80 ft

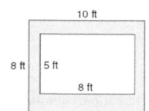

34) Mr. Jones saves $2,500 out of his monthly family income of $55,000. What fractional part of his income does he save?

   A. $\dfrac{1}{22}$

   B. $\dfrac{1}{12}$

   C. $\dfrac{3}{25}$

   D. $\dfrac{2}{15}$

35) When a number is subtracted from 24 and the difference is divided by that number, the result is 3. What is the value of the number?

   A. 2
   B. 4
   C. 6
   D. 12

36) What is the volume of a box with the following dimensions?

   Hight $= 4\ cm$ Width $= 5\ cm$ Length $= 6\ cm$

   A. $15\ cm^3$
   B. $60\ cm^3$
   C. $90\ cm^3$
   D. $120\ cm^3$

37) In two successive years, the population of a town is increased by 15% and 20%. What percent of its population is increased after two years?

   A. 32
   B. 35
   C. 38
   D. 68

38) In a school, the ratio of number of boys to girls is 4 : 5. If the number of boys is 180, what is the total number of students in the school?

   Write your answer in the box below.

39) How many tiles of 8 cm^2 is needed to cover a floor of dimension 6 cm by 24 cm?

   A. 6

   B. 12

   C. 18

   D. 24

40) The radius of the following cylinder is 8 inches and its height is 12 inches. What is the surface area of the cylinder?

   A. 96π cm^2

   B. 192π cm^2

   C. 320π cm^2

   D. 1004.8π cm^2

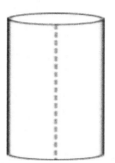

End of STAAR Grade 7 Math Practice Test

STAAR Mathematics

Practice Test 2

2020-2021

Grade 7

Total number of questions: 40

Total time to complete the test: No time limit

You may use a calculator on this practice test.

STAAR Grade 7 Mathematics Formula Sheet

LINEAR EQUATIONS

Slope – intercept form

$$y = mx + b$$

Direct Variation

$$y = kx$$

Slope of a Line

$$m = \frac{y_2 - y_1}{x_2 - x_1}$$

CIRCUMFERENCE

Circle

$$C = 2\pi r \text{ or } C = \pi d$$

AREA

Triangle

$$A = \frac{1}{2}bh$$

Parallelogram

$$A = bh$$

Trapezoid

$$A = \frac{1}{2}h(b_1 + b_2)$$

Circle

$$A = \pi r^2$$

SURFACE AREA

	Lateral	Total
Prism	$S = Ph$	$S = Ph + 2B$
Cylinder	$S = 2\pi rh$	$S = 2\pi rh + 2\pi r^2$

VOLUME

Prism or Cylinder

$$V = Bh$$

Pyramid or Cone

$$V = \frac{1}{3}Bh$$

Sphere

$$V = \frac{4}{3}\pi r^3$$

ADDITIONAL INFORMATION

Pythagorean theorem

$$a^2 + b^2 = c^2$$

Simple interest

$$I = prt$$

Compound Interest

$$A = p(1 + r)^t$$

1) If $y = 5ab + 3b^3$, what is y when $a = 2$ and $b = 3$?
   A. 24
   B. 31
   C. 51
   D. 111

2) A shirt costing $600 is discounted 25%. After a month, the shirt is discounted another 15%. Which of the following expressions can be used to find the selling price of the shirt?

   A. $(600)(0.60)$

   B. $(600) - 600\,(0.40)$

   C. $(600)(0.25) - (200)(0.15)$

   D. $(600)(0.75)(0.85)$

3) Which of the following points lies on the line $3x + 2y = 11$?

   A. $(-1, 3)$

   B. $(2, 3)$

   C. $(1, 7)$

   D. $(5, -2)$

4) What is the value of expression $-15 + 6 \times (-5) - [4 + 22 \times (-4)] \div 2 = ?$

   Write your answer in the box below.

   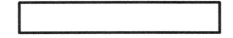

5) A taxi driver earns $9 per 1-hour work. If he works 10 hours a day and in 1 hour he uses $2-$liters petrol with price $1 for 1-liter. How much money does he earn in one day?

   A. $90

   B. $88

   C. $70

   D. $60

6) If 75% of a class are girls, and $\frac{1}{3}$ of girls take drawing class this semester, what percent of the class are girls who take drawing class this semester?

   A. 25%

   B. 28%

   C. 35%

   D. 37.5%

7) A barista averages making 18 coffees per hour. At this rate, how many hours will it take until she's made 1,800 coffees?

   A. 95 *hours*

   B. 90 *hours*

   C. 100 *hours*

   D. 105 *hours*

8) The average of $13, 15, 20$ and x is 25. What is the value of x?

   Write your answer in the box below.

9) The perimeter of the trapezoid below is $36\ cm$. What is its area?

   Write your answer in the box below.

   12 cm

   6 cm

   8 cm

10) A $50 shirt now selling for $20 is discounted by what percent?
   A. 30%
   B. 60%
   C. 70%
   D. 90%

11) If $8 < x \leq 10$, then x cannot be equal to:

    A. 8

    B. 9

    C. 9.5

    D. 10

12) Use the diagram provided as a reference. If the length between point A and C is 68, and the length between point A and B is 25, what is the length between point B and C?

    A. 31

    B. 38

    C. 41

    D. 43

13) A bag contains 20 balls: four green, five black, eight blue, a brown, a red and one white. If 19 balls are removed from the bag at random, what is the probability that a brown ball has been removed?

    A. $\frac{1}{19}$

    B. $\frac{1}{6}$

    C. $\frac{13}{20}$

    D. $\frac{19}{20}$

14) If the area of the following rectangular $ABCD$ is 160, and E is the midpoint of AB, what is the area of the shaded part?

Write your answer in the box below.

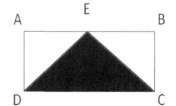

15) When a number is subtracted from 28 and the difference is divided by that number, the result is 3. What is the value of the number?

A. 2

B. 4

C. 7

D. 12

16) The volume of a cube is less than $64\ m^3$. Which of the following can be the cube's side?

A. $2\ m$

B. $4\ m$

C. $5\ m$

D. $8\ m$

17) If 60% of A is 20% of B, then B is what percent of A?

A. 3%

B. 30%

C. 200%

D. 300%

18) If Ella needed to buy 40 bottles of soda for a party in which 100 people attended, how many bottles of soda will she need to buy for a party in which 5 people are attending?

Write your answer in the box below.

19) A square has an area of $121\ cm^2$. What is its perimeter?

A. $28\ cm^2$
B. $36\ cm^2$
C. $38\ cm^2$
D. $44\ cm^2$

20) What is the surface area of the cylinder below?

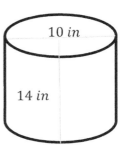

A. $95 \pi \ in^2$

B. $110 \pi \ in^2$

C. $190 \pi \ in^2$

D. $380 \pi \ in^2$

21) If $2 \leq x < 6$, what is the minimum value of the following expression?

$$3x + 1$$

A. 9

B. 7

C. 4

D. 2

22) A bank is offering 2.5% simple interest on a savings account. If you deposit $8,000, how much interest will you earn in five years?

A. $360

B. $720

C. $1,000

D. $3,600

23) A number is chosen at random from 1 to 20. Find the probability of not selecting a composite number. (A composite number is a number that is divisible by itself, 1 and at least one other whole number)

A. $\frac{1}{20}$

B. $\frac{2}{5}$

C. $\frac{9}{20}$

D. 1

24) If Logan ran 1.25 miles in 15 minutes, his average speed was?

A. $1.25 \ miles \ per \ hour$

B. $2.5 \ miles \ per \ hour$

C. $3.75 \ miles \ per \ hour$

D. $5 \ miles \ per \ hour$

25) What is the equivalent temperature of $158°F$ in Celsius? $C = \frac{5}{9}(F - 32)$

    A. 30

    B. 70

    C. 89

    D. 90

26) The cube root of 3,375 is?

    A. 155

    B. 15

    C. 7.5

    D. 5

27) Rectangle A has a length of $10\ cm$ and a width of $6\ cm$, and rectangle B has a length of $6\ cm$ and a width of $4\ cm$, what is the percent of ratio of the perimeter of rectangle B to rectangle A?

    A. 10%

    B. 20%

    C. 62%

    D. 75%

28) $\frac{1}{6b^2} + \frac{1}{6b} = \frac{1}{b^2}$, then b = ?

    A. $-\frac{16}{15}$

    B. 5

    C. $-\frac{15}{16}$

    D. 8

29) The sum of two numbers is N. If one of the numbers is 6, then what is three times the other number?

    A. $3N$

    B. $3(N - 6)$

    C. $3(N + 6)$

    D. $(N - 2)$

30) There are three equal tanks of water. If $\frac{2}{5}$ of a tank contains 200 liters of water, what is the capacity of the three tanks of water together?

A. 1,500

B. 500

C. 240

D. 80

31) Which of the following shows the numbers in decreasing order?

A. $\frac{1}{5}, \frac{5}{3}, \frac{8}{11}, \frac{2}{3}$

B. $\frac{5}{3}, \frac{8}{11}, \frac{2}{3}, \frac{1}{5}$

C. $\frac{8}{11}, \frac{2}{3}, \frac{5}{3}, \frac{1}{5}$

D. $\frac{2}{3}, \frac{8}{11}, \frac{5}{3}, \frac{1}{5}$

32) What is the slope of the line that is perpendicular to the line with equation $8x + y = 14$?

A. $\frac{1}{8}$

B. $-\frac{1}{8}$

C. $\frac{8}{12}$

D. 8

33) If $x = 7$ what's the value of $6x^2 + 5x - 13$?

A. 64

B. 316

C. 416

D. 293

34) $8\ feet, 10\ inches + 5\ feet, 12\ inches$ = how many inches?

A. $178\ inches$

B. $188\ inches$

C. $182\ inches$

D. $200\ inches$

35) Alice is choosing a menu for her lunch. She has 3 choices of appetizers, 5 choices of entrees, 6 choices of cake. How many different menu combinations are possible for her to choose?

A. 12

B. 32

C. 90

D. 120

36) The Jackson Library is ordering some bookshelves. If x is the number of bookshelves the library wants to order, which each costs \$200 and there is a one-time delivery charge of \$600, which of the following represents the total cost, in dollar, per bookshelf?

A. $\dfrac{200x+600}{x}$

B. $\dfrac{200x+600}{200}$

C. $200 + 600x$

D. $200x + 600$

37) What is the area of a square whose diagonal is 6 meters?

A. $20\ m^2$

B. $18\ m^2$

C. $12\ m^2$

D. $10\ m^2$

38) The ratio of boys to girls in a school is $3:2$. If there are 700 students in a school, how many boys are in the school?

A. 550

B. 500

C. 460

D. 420

39) The area of a circle is $121\,\pi$. What is the circumference of the circle?

    A. $11\,\pi$
    B. $12\,\pi$
    C. $22\,\pi$
    D. $44\,\pi$

40) Mr. Jones saves $1,200 out of his monthly family income of $22,800. What fractional part of his income does he save?

    A. $\frac{1}{12}$
    B. $\frac{1}{15}$
    C. $\frac{1}{19}$
    D. $\frac{1}{22}$

End of STAAR Grade 7 Math Practice Test

STAAR Mathematics Practice Tests

Answer Keys

Now, it's time to review your results to see where you went wrong and what areas you need to improve.

STAAR Math Practice Test 1				STAAR Math Practice Test 2			
1	B	21	B	1	D	21	B
2	C	22	B	2	D	22	C
3	C	23	C	3	C	23	B
4	D	24	C	4	-3	24	D
5	C	25	D	5	C	25	B
6	240	26	C	6	A	26	B
7	130	27	B	7	C	27	C
8	A	28	D	8	52	28	B
9	D	29	C	9	70	29	B
10	A	30	D	10	B	30	A
11	B	31	B	11	A	31	B
12	8	32	C	12	D	32	A
13	A	33	B	13	D	33	B
14	C	34	A	14	80	34	A
15	B	35	C	15	C	35	C
16	C	36	D	16	A	36	A
17	C	37	C	17	D	37	B
18	D	38	405	18	2	38	D
19	B	39	C	19	D	39	C
20	−30	40	D	20	C	40	C

How to score your test

The basic score on each STAAR test is the raw score, which is simply the number of questions correct. On the STAAR test each subject test should be passed individually. It means that you must meet the standard on each section of the test. If you failed one subject test but did well enough on another, that's still not a passing score.

There are four possible scores that you can receive on the STAAR Math Grade 7 Test:

Do Not Meet: This indicates that your score is lower than the passing score. If you do not pass, you can reschedule to retake any the STAAR Math test. Students have three opportunities to retake test(s) and receive remedial help if they don't pass.

Approaches: This score indicates that your score meets the standard of t

Met the Standard: This indicates that your score meets Texas state standards for that subject.

Commended Performance: This indicates that you've mastered the skills that would be taught in your grade.

There are approximately 40 questions on STAAR Mathematics for grade 7. Similar to other subject areas, you will need a minimum score to pass the Mathematics Test. There are approximately 40 raw score points on the STAAR math test. The raw points correspond with correct answers. This will then be converted into your scaled score. Approximately, you need to get 28 out of 40 raw score to pass the STAAR Mathematics for grade 7.

To score your STAAR Mathematics practice tests, first find your raw score. There were 40 questions on each STAAR Mathematics practice test in this book. All questions have one point. Use the following table to convert your raw score to the scale score.

Raw Score	Scale Score	Result	Percentile
0	1065		0
1	1197		0
2	1276		0
3	1324		0
4	1359		0
5	1387		0
6	1411		0
7	1432		1
8	1451		2
9	1468	Do Not Meet	3
10	1484		4
11	1499		6
12	1513		8
13	1526		10
14	1539		12
15	1552		14
16	1564		16
17	1576		19
18	1588		22
19	1595		25
20	1611		27
21	1622		30
22	1634		34
23	1645	Approaches	37
24	1657		41
25	1669		44
26	1681		48
27	1693		52
28	1700		55
29	1719		60
30	1733		64
31	1747		68
32	1762	Meets	72
33	1779		76
34	1796		79
35	1815		83
36	1836		87
37	1854		89
38	1889		93
39	1925	Masters	96
40 or more	1973-2185		98-100

STAAR Mathematics Practice Tests Answers and Explanations

STAAR Mathematics Practice Test 1

Answers and Explanations

1) Choice B is correct

The equation of a line in slope intercept form is: $y = \mathrm{m}x + b$. Solve for y.

$$2x - y = 12 \Rightarrow -y = 12 - 2x \Rightarrow y = (12 - 2x) \div (-1) \Rightarrow y = 2x - 6$$

The slope of this line is 2. Parallel lines have same slopes.

2) Choice C is correct.

Simplify: $5(x - 2y) + (2 - x)^2 = (5x - 10y) + (4 - 4x + x^2) = x - 10y + 4 + x^2$

When $x = 3$ and $y = -2$, therefore: $x - 10y + 4 + x^2 = 3 + 20 + 4 + 9 = 36$

3) Choice C is correct

average (mean) $= \frac{\text{sum of terms}}{\text{number of terms}} \Rightarrow 88 = \frac{\text{sum of terms}}{50} \Rightarrow sum = 88 \times 50 = 4400$

The difference of 94 and 69 is 25. Therefore, 25 should be subtracted from the sum.

$4400 - 25 = 4375.$ mean $= \frac{\text{sum of terms}}{\text{number of terms}} \Rightarrow$ mean $= \frac{4375}{50} = 87.5$

4) Choice D is correct

If the length of the box is 27, then the width of the box is one third of it, 9, and the height of the box is 3 (one third of the width). The volume of the box is:

$$V = wh = (27)(9)(3) = 729$$

5) Choice C is correct

Add the first 5 numbers. $40 + 45 + 50 + 35 + 55 = 225$. To find the distance traveled in the next 5 hours, multiply the average by number of hours. $Distance = Average \times Rate = 50 \times 5 = 250$. Add both numbers: $250 + 225 = 475$

6) The answer is 240.

The ratio of boy to girls is $2 : 3$. Therefore, there are 2 boys out of 5 students. To find the answer, first divide the total number of students by 5, then multiply the result by 2.

$$600 \div 5 = 120 \Rightarrow 120 \times 2 = 240$$

7) The answer is 130.

The perimeter of the trapezoid is 54 cm.

Therefore, the missing side (high) is $= 54 - 18 - 12 - 14 = 10$

Area of a trapezoid: $A = \frac{1}{2}h\,(b_1 + b_2) = \frac{1}{2}(10)(12 + 14) = 130$

8) Choice A is correct

Let x be the number of years. Therefore, \$2,000 per year equals $2000x$.

starting from \$24,000 annual salary means you should add that amount to $2000x$.

Income more than that is: $I > 2000x + 24000$

9) Choice D is correct.

Solve for x: $-2 \le 2x - 4 < 8 \Rightarrow$ (add 4 all sides) $-2 + 4 \le 2x - 4 + 4 < 8 + 4 \Rightarrow$

$2 \le 2x < 12 \Rightarrow$ (divide all sides by 2) $1 \le x < 6$. x is between 1 and 6.

10) Choice A is correct.

Let x be the number of new shoes the team can purchase. Therefore, the team can purchase $120\,x$. The team had \$20,000 and spent \$14000. Now the team can spend on new shoes \$6000 at most. Now, write the inequality: $120x + 14.000 \le 20.000$

11) Choice B is correct.

The options to get sum of 6: $(1\ \&\ 5)$ and $(5\ \&\ 1), (2\ \&\ 4)$ and $(4\ \&\ 2), (3\ \&\ 3)$, so we have 5 options. The options to get sum of 9: $(3\ \&\ 6)$ and $(6\ \&\ 3), (4\ \&\ 5)$ and $(5\ \&\ 4)$, we have 4 options. To get the sum of 6 or 9 for two dice, we have 9 options: $5 + 4 = 9$

Since, we have $6 \times 6 = 36$ total options, the probability of getting a sum of 6 and 9 is 9 out of 36 or $\frac{9}{36} = \frac{1}{4}$.

12) The answer is 8.

Use formula of rectangle prism volume: $V = (length)(width)(height)$

$$\Rightarrow 2000 = (25)(10)(height) \Rightarrow height = 2000 \div 250 = 8$$

13) Choice A is correct

In the scale model of a building 3 inches represents 45 feet. Therefore, 1.5 feet (18 inches) of the scale model represents 270 feet. Write a proportion and solve:

$$\frac{3\ inches}{45\ feet} = \frac{18\ inches}{x} \rightarrow x = \frac{18 \times 45}{3} = 270\ feet$$

14) Choice C is correct

Use simple interest formula: $I = prt$ (I = interest, p = principal, r = rate, t = time)

$$I = (8000)(0.045)(5) = 1800$$

15) Choice B is correct

The probability of choosing a Clubs is $\frac{13}{52} = \frac{1}{4}$

16) Choice C is correct

Use distance formula: $Distance = Rate \times time \Rightarrow 420 = 50 \times T$, divide both sides by 50. $420 / 50 = T \Rightarrow T = 8.4$ hours. Change hours to minutes for the decimal part. $0.4\ hours = 0.4 \times 60 = 24\ minutes$.

17) Choice C is correct.

$$11 \times 36 + 6 \times 12 + 4 = 472$$

18) Choice D is correct.

To find the discount, multiply the number by $(100\% -$ rate of discount).

Therefore, for the first discount we get: $(200)(100\% - 15\%) = (200)(0.85) = 170$

For the next 15% discount: $(200)(0.85)(0.85)$

19) Choice B is correct.

Input $(-1, 3)$ in the $2x + 4y = 10$ formula instead of x and y. So we have:

$$2(-1) + 4(3) = 10 \rightarrow -2 + 12 = 10$$

20) The answer is: -30

Use PEMDAS (order of operation): $5 + 8 \times (-2) - [4 + 22 \times 5] \div 6 =$

$$5 + 8 \times (-2) - [4 + 110] \div 6 = 5 + 8 \times (-2) - [114] \div 6 = 5 + (-16) - 19$$
$$= 5 + (-16) - 19 = -11 - 19 = -30$$

21) Choice B is correct.

Use this formula: Percent of Change: $\frac{New\ Value - Old\ Value}{Old\ Value} \times 100\%$

$\frac{16000-20000}{20000} \times 100\% = 20\%$ and $\frac{12800-16000}{16000} \times 100\% = 20\%$

22) Choice B is correct

Plug in 104 for F and then solve for C.

$C = \frac{5}{9}(F - 32) \Rightarrow C = \frac{5}{9}(104 - 32) \Rightarrow C = \frac{5}{9}(72) = 40$

23) Choice C is correct

The square of a number is $\frac{25}{64}$, then the number is the square root of $\frac{25}{64}$

$\sqrt{\frac{25}{64}} = \frac{5}{8}$, The cube of the number is: $(\frac{5}{8})^3 = \frac{125}{512}$

24) Choice C is correct

Surface Area of a cylinder $= 2\pi r(r + h)$, the radius of the cylinder is 3 $(6 \div 2)$ inches and its height is 8 inches. Therefore, Surface Area of a cylinder $= 2\pi(3)(3 + 8) = 66\pi$

25) Choice D is correct.

$\frac{2}{3}x + \frac{1}{6} = \frac{1}{3} \Rightarrow \frac{2}{3}x = \frac{1}{6} \Rightarrow x = \frac{1}{6} \times \frac{3}{2} \Rightarrow x = \frac{1}{4}$

26) Choice C is correct

Solve for the sum of five numbers: average $= \frac{\text{sum of terms}}{\text{number of terms}} \Rightarrow 24 = \frac{\text{sum of 5 numbers}}{5}$

$\Rightarrow sum\ of\ 5\ numbers = 24 \times 5 = 120$. The sum of 5 numbers is 120. If a sixth number 42 is added, then the sum of 6 numbers is $120 + 42 = 162$

$average = \frac{\text{sum of terms}}{\text{number of terms}} = \frac{162}{6} = 27$

27) Choice B is correct.

$Probability = \frac{\text{number of desired outcomes}}{\text{number of total outcomes}} = \frac{18}{12+18+18+24} = \frac{18}{72} = \frac{1}{4}$

28) Choice D is correct

Change the numbers to decimal and then compare. $\frac{2}{3} = 0.666 \dots , 0.68 , 67\% = 0.67$

$\frac{4}{5} = 0.80$ Therefore $\frac{4}{5} > 68\% > 0.67 > \frac{2}{3}$

29) Choice C is correct

To find the number of possible outfit combinations, multiply number of options for each factor: $3 \times 5 \times 4 = 60$

30) Choice D is correct

$4 \div \frac{1}{6} = 24$

31) Choice B is correct

The diagonal of the square is 8. Let x be the side. Use Pythagorean Theorem: $a^2 + b^2 = c^2$

$x^2 + x^2 = 82 \Rightarrow 2x^2 = 82 \Rightarrow 2x^2 = 64 \Rightarrow x^2 = 32 \Rightarrow x = \sqrt{32}$

The area of the square is: $\sqrt{32} \times \sqrt{32} = 32$

32) Choice C is correct

The ratio of boy to girls is $4 : 7$. Therefore, there are 4 boys out of 11 students. To find the answer, first divide the total number of students by 11, then multiply the result by 4.

$44 \div 11 = 4 \Rightarrow 4 \times 4 = 16$. There are 16 boys and 28 $(44 - 16)$ girls. So, 12 more boys should be enrolled to make the ratio $1 : 1$

33) Choice B is correct

Use the area of rectangle formula $(s = a \times b)$.

To find area of the shaded region subtract the smaller rectangle from bigger rectangle.

$$S_1 - S_2 = (10\,ft \times 8ft) - (5ft \times 8ft) \Rightarrow S_1 - S_2 = 40ft$$

34) Choice A is correct.

2,500 out of 55,000 equals to $\frac{2500}{55000} = \frac{25}{550} = \frac{1}{22}$

35) Choice C is correct.

Let the number be x. Then: $\frac{24 - x}{x} = 3 \rightarrow 3x = 24 - x \rightarrow 4x = 24 \rightarrow x = 6$

36) Choice D is correct.

$Volume\ of\ a\ box = length \times width \times height = 4 \times 5 \times 6 = 120$

37) Choice C is correct

The population is increased by 15% and 20%. 15% increase changes the population to 115% of original population. For the second increase, multiply the result by 120%.

$(1.15) \times (1.20) = 1.38 = 138\%$. 38 percent of the population is increased after two years.

38) The answer is 405.

The ratio of boy to girls is $4 : 5$. Therefore, there are 4 boys out of 9 students. To find the answer, first divide the number of boys by 4, then multiply the result by 9.

$$180 \div 4 = 45 \Rightarrow 45 \times 9 = 405$$

39) Choice C is correct

The area of the floor is: $6\ cm \times 24\ cm = 144\ cm^2$

The number of tiles needed $= 144 \div 8 = 18$

40) Choices D is correct.

Surface Area of a cylinder $= 2\pi r(r + h)$,

The radius of the cylinder is 8 inches and its height is 12 inches. π is about 3.14. Then:

$Surface\ Area\ of\ a\ cylinder = 2(\pi)(8)(8 + 12) = 320\pi = 1004.8$

STAAR Mathematics Practice Test 2

Answers and Explanations

1) Choice D is correct

$y = 5ab + 3b^3$. Plug in the values of a and b in the equation: $a = 2$ and $b = 3$.

$y = 5\ (2)(3) + 3\ (3)^3 = 30 + 3(27) = 30 + 81 = 111$

2) Choice D is correct

To find the discount, multiply the number by $(100\% - rate\ of\ discount)$.

Therefore, for the first discount we get: $(600)\ (100\% - 25\%) = (600)\ (0.75)$

For the next 15% discount: $(600)(0.75)(0.85)$

3) Choices D is correct

$3x + 2y = 11$. Plug in the values of x and y from choices provided. Then:

A. $(-1, 3)$ $3x + 2y = 11 \rightarrow 3(-1) + 2(3) = 11 \rightarrow -3 + 6 = 11$ NOT true!

B. $(2, 3)$ $3x + 2y = 11 \rightarrow 3(2) + 2(3) = 11 \rightarrow 6 + 6 = 11$ NOT true!

C. $(1, 7)$ $3x + 2y = 11 \rightarrow 3(1) + 2(7) = 11 \rightarrow 3 + 14 = 11$ NOT true!

D. $(5, -2)$ $3x + 2y = 11 \rightarrow 3(5) + 2(-2) = 11 \rightarrow 15 - 4 = 11$ Yes!

4) The answer is -3.

Use PEMDAS (order of operation): $-15 + 6 \times (-5) - [4 + 22 \times (-4)] \div 2 =$

$$-15 - 30 - [4 - 88] \div 2 = -45 - [-84] \div 2 = -45 + 84 \div 2 = -45 + 42 = -3$$

5) Choice C is correct

$9 \times 10 = \$90$. Petrol use: $10 \times 2 = 20$ liters.   Petrol cost: $20 \times \$1 = \$20$

Money earned: $\$90 - \$20 = \$70$

6) Choice A is correct

The percent of girls take drawing class is: $75\% \times \frac{1}{3} = 25\%$

7) Choice C is correct

$\frac{1 \ hour}{18 \ coffees} = \frac{x}{1,800} \Rightarrow 18 \times x = 1 \times 1,800 \Rightarrow 18x = 1,800 \Rightarrow x = 100$

It takes 100 hours until she's made 1,800 coffees.

8) The answer is 52.

$average = \frac{sum \ of \ terms}{number \ of \ terms} \Rightarrow 25 = \frac{13+15+20+}{4} \Rightarrow 100 = 48 + x \Rightarrow x = 52$

9) The answer is 70.

The perimeter of the trapezoid is $36 \ cm$.

Therefore, the missing side (height) is = $36 - 8 - 12 - 6 = 10$

Area of a trapezoid: $A = \frac{1}{2} h (b_1 + b_2) = \frac{1}{2} (10) (6 + 8) = 70$

10) Choice B is correct

Use the formula for Percent of Change: $\frac{New \ Value - Old \ Value}{Old \ Value} \times 100\%$

$\frac{20-50}{50} \times 100\% = -60\%$ (negative sign here means that the new price is less than old price).

11) Choice A is correct

$8 < x \leq 10$, then x cannot be equal to 8.

12) Choice D is correct

$68 - 25 = 43$

13) Choice D is correct

If 20 balls are removed from the bag at random, there will be one ball in the bag. The probability of choosing a brown ball is 1 out of 20. Therefore, the probability of not choosing a brown ball is 19 out of 20 and the probability of having not a brown ball after removing 19 balls is the same.

14) The answer is 80.

Since, E is the midpoint of AB, then the area of all triangles DAE, DEF, CFE and CBE are equal. Let x be the area of one of the triangle, then: $4x = 160 \rightarrow x = 40$

The area of $DEC = 2x = 2(40) = 80$

15) Choice C is correct

Let x be the number. Write the equation and solve for x. $(28 - x) \div x = 3$

Multiply both sides by x. $(28 - x) = 3x$, then add x both sides. $28 = 4x$, now divide both sides by 4. $x = 7$

16) Choice A is correct

Volume of the cube is less than $64 \ m^3$. Use the formula of volume of cubes.

$volume = (one \ side)^3 \Rightarrow 64 > \Rightarrow 64 > (one \ side)^3$. Find the cube root of both sides. Then: $4 > one \ side$. The side of the cube is less than 4. Only choice A is less than 4.

17) Choice D is correct

Write the equation and solve for B: $0.60 \ A = 0.20 \ B$, divide both sides by 0.20, then:

$\frac{0.60}{0.20} A = B$, therefore: $B = 3 \ A$, and B is 3 times of A or it's 300% of A.

18) The answer is 2.

$\frac{40}{100} = \frac{x}{5} \rightarrow x = \frac{40 \times 5}{100} = 2$

19) Choice D is correct

$Area = side^2 \rightarrow 121 = side^2 \rightarrow side = 11$
$Perimeter = 4 \times side \rightarrow Perimeter = 4 \times 11 = 44$

20) Choice C is correct

Surface Area of a cylinder $= 2\pi r(r + h)$, the radius of the cylinder is $5(10 \div 2)$ inches and its height is 14 inches. Therefore, Surface Area of a cylinder $= 2\pi(5)(5 + 14) = 190\pi$

21) Choice B is correct
$2 \leq x < 6 \rightarrow$ Multiply all sides of the inequality by 3. Then: $2 \times 3 \leq 3 \times x < 6 \times 3 \rightarrow$

$6 \leq 3x < 18$. Add 1 to all sides. Then: $\rightarrow 6 + 1 \leq 3x + 1 < 18 + 1 \rightarrow 7 \leq 3x + 1 < 19$

Minimum value of $3x + 1$ is 7.

22) Choice C is correct

Use simple interest formula: $I = prt \ (I = interest, \ p = principal, \ r = rate, \ t = time)$

$I = (8,000)(0.025)(5) = 1,000$

23) Choice B is correct

Set of numbers that are not composite between 1 and 20: $A = \{2, 3, 5, 7, 11, 13, 17, 19\}$

$Probability = \frac{number\ of\ desired\ outcomes}{number\ of\ total\ outcomes} = \frac{8}{20} = \frac{2}{5}$

24) Choice D is correct

His average speed was: $\frac{1.25}{0.25} = 5$ miles per hour

25) Choice B is correct

Plug in 158 for F and then solve for C. $C = \frac{5}{9}(F - 32) \Rightarrow C = \frac{5}{9}(158 - 32) \Rightarrow$

$C = \frac{5}{9}(126) = 70$

26) Choice B is correct

Factor the number: $3,375 = 15^3$, $\sqrt[3]{15^3} = 15$, Then: $\sqrt[3]{3,375} = 15$

27) Choice C is correct

Perimeter of rectangle A is equal to: $2 \times (10 + 6) = 2 \times 16 = 32$

Perimeter of rectangle B is equal to: $2 \times (6 + 4) = 2 \times 10 = 20$

Therefore: $\frac{20}{32} \times 100 = 0.62 \times 100 = 62\%$

28) Choice B is correct

Subtract $\frac{1}{6b}$ and $\frac{1}{b^2}$ from both sides of the equation. Then:

$\frac{1}{6b^2} + \frac{1}{6b} = \frac{1}{b^2} \rightarrow \frac{1}{6b^2} - \frac{1}{b^2} = -\frac{1}{6b}$

Multiply both numerator and denominator of the fraction $\frac{1}{b^2}$ by 6. Then: $\frac{1}{6b^2} - \frac{6}{6b^2} = -\frac{1}{6b}$

Simplify the first side of the equation: $-\frac{5}{6b^2} = -\frac{1}{6b}$

Use cross multiplication method: $30b = 6b^2 \rightarrow 30 = 6b \rightarrow b = 5$

29) Choice B is correct

Let x and y be the numbers. Then:

$x + y = N$, $x = 6 \rightarrow 6 + y = N \rightarrow y = N - 6$, $3y = 3(N - 6)$

30) Choice A is correct

Let x be the capacity of one tank. Then, $\frac{2}{5}x = 200 \rightarrow x = \frac{200 \times 5}{2} = 500$ Liters

The amount of water in three tanks is equal to: $3 \times 500 = 1,500$ Liters

31) Choice B is correct

$\frac{1}{5} \cong 0.2$ $\qquad$ $\frac{5}{3} \cong 1.66$ $\qquad$ $\frac{8}{11} \cong 0.73$ $\qquad$ $\frac{2}{3} = 0.66$

$$\frac{5}{3} > \frac{8}{11} > \frac{2}{3} > \frac{1}{5}$$

32) Choice A is correct

The equation of a line in slope intercept form is: $y = mx + b$, Solve for y: $8x + y = 14 \Rightarrow y = -8x + 14$, The slope of this line is -8. The slope of the line perpendicular to this line is:

$$m_1 \times m_2 = -1 \Rightarrow -8 \times m_2 = -1 \Rightarrow m_2 = \frac{1}{8}$$

33) Choice B is correct

Plug in the value of x in the expression. Then: $6x^2 + 5x - 13 = 6(7)^2 + 5(7) - 13 = 316$

34) Choice A is correct

$1 \, feet = 12 \, inches.$ $\quad$ $8 \, feet, 10 \, inches = 106 \, inches$, $5 \, feet, 12 \, inches = 72 \, inches$

$10 + 72 = 178$

35) Choice C is correct

To find the number of possible outfit combinations, multiply number of options for each factor:

$3 \times 5 \times 6 = 90$

36) Choice A is correct

The amount of money for x bookshelf is: $\quad$ $200x$, Then, the total cost of all bookshelves is equal to: $\quad$ $200x + 600$, The total cost, in dollar, per bookshelf is: $\frac{Total \ cost}{number \ of \ items} = \frac{200x + 600}{x}$

37) Choice B is correct

The diagonal of the square is 6 meters. Let x be the side. Use Pythagorean Theorem:

$$a^2 + b^2 = c^2 \Rightarrow x^2 + x^2 = 6^2 \Rightarrow 2x^2 = 6^2 \Rightarrow 2x^2 = 36 \Rightarrow x^2 = 18 \Rightarrow x = \sqrt{18}$$

The area of the square is: $\sqrt{18} \times \sqrt{18} = 18 \, m^2$

38) Choice D is correct

The ratio of boys to girls is $3: 2$. Therefore, there are 3 boys out of 5 students. To find the answer, first divide the total number of students by 5, then multiply the result by 3.

$700 \div 5 = 140 \Rightarrow 140 \times 3 = 420$

39) Choice C is correct

Use the formula of the area of circles. $Area = \pi r^2 \Rightarrow 121 \pi = \pi r^2 \Rightarrow 121 = r^2 \Rightarrow r = 11$

Radius of the circle is 11. Now, use the circumference formula:

Circumference $= 2\pi r = 2\pi\,(11) = 22\,\pi$

40) Choice C is correct

1,200 out of 22,800 equals to $\dfrac{1,200}{22,800} = \dfrac{12}{228} = \dfrac{1}{19}$

www.EffortlessMath.com

... So Much More Online!

✓ FREE Math lessons

✓ More Math learning books!

✓ Mathematics Worksheets

✓ Online Math Tutors

Need a PDF version of this book?

Visit www.EffortlessMath.com

Receive the PDF version of this book or get another FREE book!

Thank you for using our Book!

Do you LOVE this book?

Then, you can get the PDF version of this book or another book absolutely FREE!

Please email us at:

info@EffortlessMath.com

for details.

Made in the USA
Middletown, DE
04 May 2022

65292936R00066